All-in-One
Student Workbook

Grade 2

Includes:

- Review of key concepts/skills

- Practice for each lesson

- Reteaching for each lesson

D1278489

Scott Foresman·Addison Wesley
enVisionMATH™

Learning Solutions

New York   Boston   San Francisco
London   Toronto   Sydney   Tokyo   Singapore   Madrid
Mexico City   Munich   Paris   Cape Town   Hong Kong   Montreal

This special edition published in cooperation with Pearson Learning Solutions.

All trademarks, service marks, registered trademarks, and registered service marks are the property of their respective owners and are used herein for identification purposes only.

Pearson Learning Solutions, 501 Boylston Street, Suite 900, Boston, MA 02116
A Pearson Education Company
www.pearsoned.com

Printed in the United States of America

8 9 10   V001   16 15

000200010270780083

CP

ISBN-10: 0-328-62589-2
ISBN-13: 978-0-328-62589-5

Table of Contents

Review From Last Year

Name _____

Sorting and Classifying

These shapes are the same. | So, this shape belongs with them.

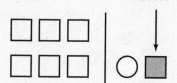

These shapes are all shaded. | So, this shape belongs with them.

Circle the shape that goes with the group.

1. |

2. |

3.  |

4. |

5. Draw a shape that goes with the group.

Notes for Home Your child sorted shapes by color and size. *Home Activity:* Ask your child to sort common objects at home, such as buttons or coins, by color and size.

Name _____

Problem Solving: Graphing

Make a bar graph. Color a square for each playground item.

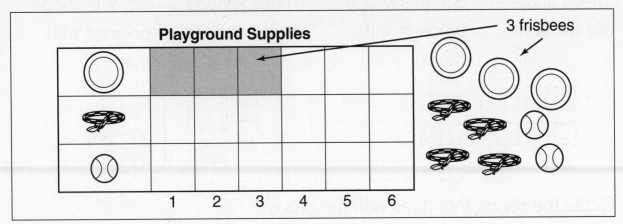

3 frisbees

Playground Supplies

1. Complete the bar graph above.

2. How many more than ◯ ? _____

3. How many fewer ◯◯ than ◯ ? _____

Complete the bar graph below. Answer the questions.

4.

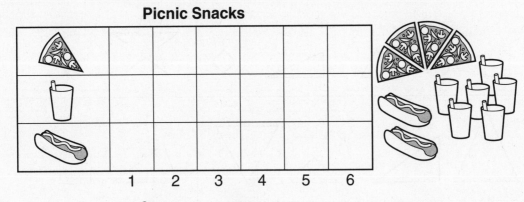

Picnic Snacks

5. How many more ▢ than 🍕 ? _____

6. How many fewer 🌭 than 🍕 ? _____

7. How many picnic snacks in all? _____

Notes for Home Your child created and used a bar graph. *Home Activity:* Ask your child to make a bar graph of two types of objects at home.

Name _____

Explore Addition and Subtraction

There are 3 🐱 .

5 more 🐱 come.
How many in all?

Use counters.

①②③ ④⑤⑥⑦⑧

3 + 5 = 8

There are 7 🐶 .

2 🐶 run away.
How many are left?

Use counters.

①②③④⑤⑥̷⑦̷

7 − 2 = 5

Solve each problem. Use counters.

1. A table has 6 🪑 .

   2 🪑 are taken away.
   How many are left?

   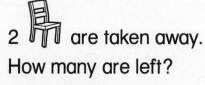

   ## 6 − 2 = _____

2. There a 4 🥦

   in Lee's yard.
   He planted 5 new .
   How many in all?

   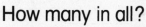

   ## 4 + 5 = _____

3. Mick has 5 ✏️ .

   He lost 3 ✏️ .

   How many are left?

   ## 5 − 3 = _____

4. A pond has 2 🐸 .

   4 🐸 came to the pond.

   How many in all?

   ## 2 + 4 = _____

5. There were 3 birds on a branch.

   6 more birds came. How many in all?   _____

Addition Sentences to 12

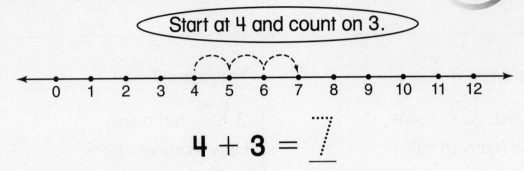

Start at 4 and count on 3.

$$4 + 3 = \underline{7}$$

Use the number line. Write the sum.

1. $8 + 1 = \underline{9}$ $4 + 6 = \underline{}$ $5 + 2 = \underline{}$

2. $3 + 5 = \underline{}$ $7 + 0 = \underline{}$ $9 + 2 = \underline{}$

3. $1 + 8 = \underline{}$ $6 + 5 = \underline{}$ $4 + 3 = \underline{}$

4. $3 + 1 = \underline{}$ $4 + 2 = \underline{}$ $3 + 9 = \underline{}$

5.
$$
\begin{array}{ccccccc}
1 & 2 & 4 & 9 & 3 & 0 & 6 \\
+7 & +1 & +5 & +1 & +7 & +8 & +3 \\
\hline
\end{array}
$$

6. Choose any number.
   Count on 3
   Write your answer. $\underline{} + 3 = \underline{}$

Notes for Home Your child used a number line to add numbers. *Home Activity:* Write three problems such as 3 + 6, 4 + 3, and 8 + 4, and ask your child to find the sums using a number line.

4

Subtraction Sentences to 12

Start at 9. Count back 3.

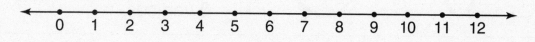

$$9 - 3 = 6$$

Use the number line. Write the difference.

1. $8 - 2 = 6$ $5 - 3 = \_\_\_$ $7 - 4 = \_\_\_$

2. $6 - 1 = \_\_\_$ $9 - 4 = \_\_\_$ $3 - 3 = \_\_\_$

3. $6 - 0 = \_\_\_$ $11 - 5 = \_\_\_$ $8 - 5 = \_\_\_$

4. $4 - 2 = \_\_\_$ $10 - 7 = \_\_\_$ $7 - 6 = \_\_\_$

5.
$$\begin{array}{ccccccc} 2 & 5 & 12 & 9 & 8 & 11 & 12 \\ -2 & -4 & -6 & -7 & -6 & -0 & -9 \\ \hline \end{array}$$

6. Katie had 12 kittens. She gave away
4 kittens. How many did she have left?   _____

Notes for Home Your child subtracted by counting back. *Home Activity:* Write three problems such as 9 – 3, 10 – 5, and 12 – 4, and ask your child to count back on a number line to find the differences.

Name _____

Solids and Shapes

Review
6

Solid	Flat surface of solid	
		The flat surface of the solid has **4** straight sides and **4** vertices.
		The flat surface of the solid has **0** straight sides and **0** vertices.

Draw the shape of the flat surface.

Tell how many straight sides and vertices each shape has.

Solid	Shape of flat surface	Straight Sides	Vertices
	▭		

Notes for Home Your child reviewed solids and shapes in solids. *Home Activity:* Ask your child to identify shapes and solids in objects at home. Have them count the straight sides and vertices on these objects.

6

Fractions

one half $\frac{1}{2}$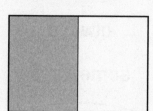

one third $\frac{1}{3}$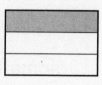

one fourth $\frac{1}{4}$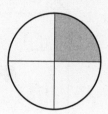

Write the letter for each fraction.

A.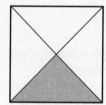

B.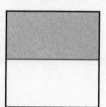

C.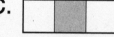

1. The shape that shows one half is   _B_

2. The shape that shows one third is   _____

3. The shape that shows one fourth is   _____

Color each to show the fraction.

4.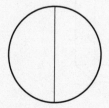

one half $\frac{1}{2}$

5.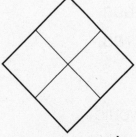

one fourth $\frac{1}{4}$

6.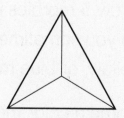

one third $\frac{1}{3}$

Notes for Home Your child reviewed halves, thirds, and fourths. *Home Activity:* Ask your child to cut pieces of bread to show halves, thirds, and fourths.

Name _____

Probability

Tell whether you will always, sometimes, or never pick a shape.

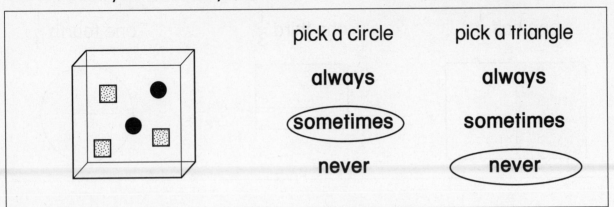

pick a circle

always

(sometimes)

never

pick a triangle

always

sometimes

(never)

What will happen with each bag? Circle the word.

1. Pick a star.

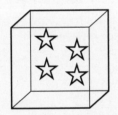

always

sometimes

never

2. Pick a wheel.

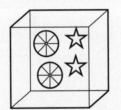

always

sometimes

never

3. Pick a marble.

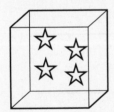

always

sometimes

never

4. Pick a yo-yo.

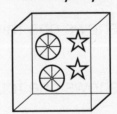

always

sometimes

never

5. Draw 5 marbles in your bag so you sometimes get a red, yellow, or blue marble.

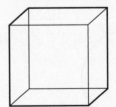

6. Name a color that you would never pick from your bag.

_____

Notes for Home Your child described how likely it was to pick a given object from a bag. *Home Activity:* Place objects such as coins or buttons in a paper bag. Ask your child whether an object will always, sometimes, or never be picked.

Name _____

Numbers to 60

2 tens   and   **6** extra   is **26**.

Circle groups of 10. Write the number.

1.

_____ tens and _____ extra is _____.

2.

_____ tens and _____ extra is _____.

3.

_____ tens and _____ extra is _____.

Write the missing numbers.

4. 27, 28, 29, _____, _____, _____, _____, _____, _____

5. 52, 53, 54, _____, _____, _____, _____, _____, _____

Notes for Home Your child put things in groups of ten and wrote the number. *Home Activity:* Have your child count a handful of pennies or buttons by putting them in groups of ten.

Skip Counting

Count the snowflakes by 2s.

2,   4,   6,   8,   10

1. Count the fingers by 5s.

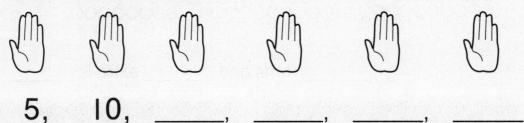

5,   10, _____, _____, _____, _____

2. Count the stars by 10s.

_____, _____, _____, _____, _____, _____

3. Count by 5s.

20, 25, _____, _____, _____, _____, _____

4. Count by 10s.

30, 40, _____, _____, _____, _____, _____, _____

5. Count by 2s.

34, 36, _____, _____, _____, _____, _____, _____

Notes for Home Your child practiced counting by 2s, 5s, and 10s. *Home Activity:* Ask your child to count by 2s to 20, 5s to 50, and 10s to 100.

Name _____

Numbers to 100

The number 64 comes after 63 and before 65.

60	61	62	63	64	65	66	67	68	69

Write the missing numbers.

1	2	3				8		
		14		17				20
	22			26				
		33					39	
41			45					
		54						60
	62				67			
	73						79	
81								90
		94			98			

Write the missing numbers.

1. 70, 71, 72, _____, _____, _____, _____, _____, _____

2. _____, _____, _____, 96, 97, _____, _____, _____

Notes for Home Your child used the patterns in a 100 chart to help find missing numbers. *Home Activity:* Ask your child to write the 3 numbers just before and just after 50. (47, 48, 49; 51, 52, 53)

11

Name _____

Money

 = 25¢, = 10¢, = 5¢, = 1¢

Count. Write the amount of the coins.

1.

25,   35,   40, 45,   46, 47, 48

Start.   Count by 10s,   by 5s,   and by 1s.

 **48** ¢

2.

25, 35, ____, ____, ____, ____,

☐ ¢

3.

____, ____, ____, ____, ____, ____

 ¢

4.

____, ____, ____, ____, ____, ____

 ¢

5. Draw 6 coins to make 18¢.

Time

Write the time.

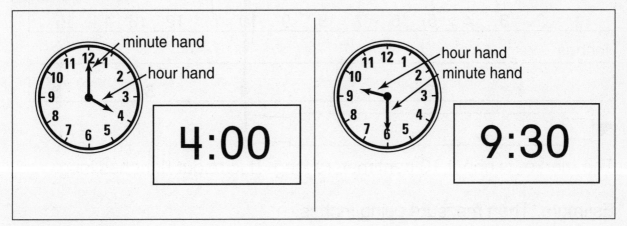

Write the time.

1.
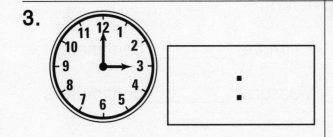

2.
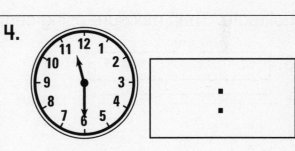

3.

4.

5.
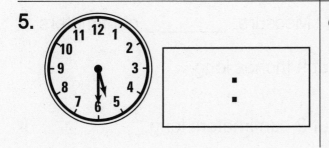

6.

© Pearson Education, Inc. 2

Notes for Home Your child read and wrote time to the half hour. *Home Activity:* Practice telling time to the half hour at home using clocks and watches. Ask your child to write the time shown.

Name _____

Length

centimeters

| | 1 | 2 | 3 | 4 | 5 | 6 | 7 | 8 | 9 | 10 | 11 | 12 | 13 | 14 | 15 |

inches

| | | 1 | | 2 | | 3 | 4 | | 5 | | 6 |

The marker is about 10 centimeters long. It is about 4 inches long.

Estimate. Then measure using inches.

1.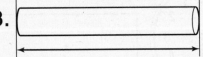

Estimate. _____ inches

Measure. _____ inches

2.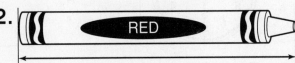

RED

Estimate. _____ inches

Measure. _____ inches

Estimate. Then measure using centimeters.

3.

Estimate. _____ centimeters

Measure. _____ centimeters

4.

Estimate. _____ centimeters

Measure. _____ centimeters

5. Start at the dot. Draw a line about 4 inches long.

•

6. Start at the dot. Draw a line about 8 centimeters long.

•

Notes for Home Your child estimated and measured objects using an inch and centimeter ruler. *Home Activity:* Have your child estimate and measure the lengths of small household objects such as spoons and forks.

Name _____

Weight

A telephone weighs about **1 kilogram.**

A loaf of bread weighs about **1 pound.**

How heavy would each be? Circle the best answer.

1.

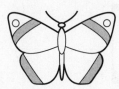

lighter than 1 kilogram
about 1 kilogram
heavier than 1 kilogram

2.

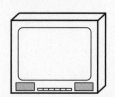

lighter than 1 pound
about 1 pound
heavier than 1 pound

3.

lighter than 1 kilogram
about 1 kilogram
heavier than 1 kilogram

4.

lighter than 1 pound
about 1 pound
heavier than 1 pound

5.

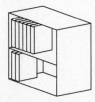

lighter than 1 kilogram
about 1 kilogram
heavier than 1 kilogram

6.

lighter than 1 pound
about 1 pound
heavier than 1 pound

Notes for Home Your child compared the weight of objects to a pound or a kilogram. *Home Activity:* Find a food product such as a can of soup that weighs about a pound or a kilogram. Have your child compare the weight of that object to other objects.

Capacity

A toy bucket holds about **I quart.**

A water bottle holds about **I liter.**

How much would each hold? Circle the best answer.

1.

less then I quart
about I quart
more than I quart

2.

less than I liter
about I liter
more than I liter

3.

less than I quart
about I quart
more than I quart

4.

less then I liter
about I liter
more than I liter

5.

less then I quart
about I quart
more than I quart

6.

less than I liter
about I liter
more than I liter

Notes for Home Your child checked whether containers would hold more or less than a gallon or a liter.
Home Activity: Find containers at home which have customary and metric measurement markings. Have your child compare the capacity of the containers to a gallon or a liter.

Name _____

Addition to 18

Find 8 + 5.

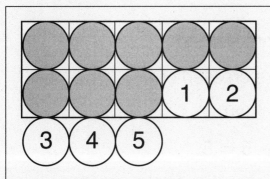

8 are shaded.

2 more fill the 10 frame.

3 more give 13.

8 + 5 = 13.

Find each sum.

1.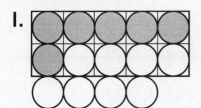

2.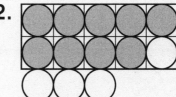

$6 + 8 =$ _____ $9 + 4 =$ _____

3. $9 + 5 =$ _____ $6 + 7 =$ _____ $12 + 6 =$ _____

4. $9 + 7 =$ _____ $9 + 8 =$ _____ $10 + 4 =$ _____

5. $7 + 7 =$ _____ $9 + 9 =$ _____ $4 + 13 =$ _____

6. $7 + 6 =$ _____ $8 + 8 =$ _____ $6 + 10 =$ _____

7. Kevin walked 6 blocks to the library.

Then he walked 8 blocks to school.

How many blocks did he walk in all?   _____

Notes for Home Your child added sums to 18 by making a 10 first. *Home Activity:* Ask your child to draw a picture and write a number sentence for the last problem on the page.

Subtraction to 18

Find 13 − 5.

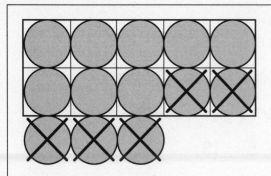

13 are shaded.

5 are crossed out.

8 are left.

13 − 5 = 8.

Find each difference.

1.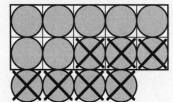

14 − 7 = ____

2.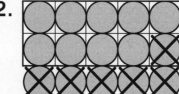

15 − 6 = ____

3. 9 − 6 = ____   16 − 0 = ____   7 − 5 = ____

4. 8 − 3 = ____   18 − 9 = ____   17 − 0 = ____

5. 13 − 6 = ____   12 − 8 = ____   11 − 9 = ____

6. 11 − 4 = ____   14 − 9 = ____   16 − 9 = ____

7. Maria had 14 pencils. She gave 6 away.
    How many did she have left?   _____

Notes for Home Your child subtracted facts such as 9 − 6 and 14 − 9. *Home Activity:* Ask your child to draw a
picture and write a number sentence for the last problem on the page.

© Pearson Education, Inc. 2

Name _____

Two-Digit Addition

Find 24 + 15.

First add the **ones**.	Then add the **tens**.

tens	ones
2	4
+ 1	5
	9

tens	ones
2	4
+ 1	5
3	9

Add.

1.

tens	ones
3	2
+ 2	6

2.

tens	ones
3	3
+ 4	2

3.
```
  15        35        17        28
+ 42      + 12      + 52      + 60
```

4.
```
  44        60        29         8
+ 55      + 37      + 50      + 51
```

5.
```
  47        81        62        77
+ 50      + 11      + 15      + 21
```

6. Joan read 34 pages of her book. Later, she read 45 more pages. How many pages did she read? _____

Name _____

Two-Digit Subtraction

Find 45 − 12.

First subtract the **ones.**			Then subtract the **tens.**		

tens	ones
4	5
− 1	2
	3

tens	ones
4	5
− 1	2
3	3

Subtract.

1.

tens	ones
3	7
− 2	4

2.

tens	ones
6	4
− 4	3

3.

$$56 - 22$$ $$29 - 5$$ $$48 - 13$$ $$73 - 60$$

4.

$$90 - 50$$ $$37 - 27$$ $$58 - 50$$ $$61 - 41$$

5.

$$44 - 33$$ $$97 - 46$$ $$65 - 54$$ $$16 - 12$$

6. Bill had 47 marbles. He gave 15 away.

How many marbles does he have left? _____

Notes for Home Your child subtracted numbers like 56 − 22. *Home Activity:* Ask your child to tell a subtraction math story for one of the problems on the page.

Reteaching and Practice

Writing Addition Number Sentences

How many counters are there in all?
Add the parts.

$2 + 4 = 6$
is called an
addition sentence.

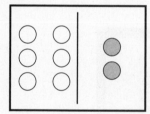

__2__ and __4__ is __6__

| Part | Part | Whole |

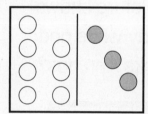

__2__ plus __4__ equals __6__ .

__2__ + __4__ = __6__

Write the addition sentence for each problem.

1.

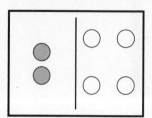

How many counters in all?

____ + ____ = ____

2.

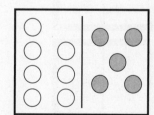

How many counters in all?

____ + ____ = ____

3.

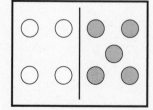

How many counters in all?

____ + ____ = ____

4.

How many counters in all?

____ + ____ = ____

Writing Addition Number Sentences

Write an addition sentence for the picture.

1.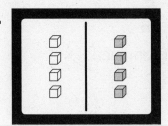

$\underline{4} + \underline{4} = \underline{8}$

2.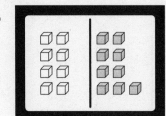

___ + ___ = ___

3. Ann has 5 white rocks. She also has 6 gray rocks. Which picture shows how many white and gray rocks Ann has?

Ⓐ

Ⓑ

Ⓒ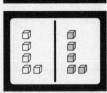

Ⓓ

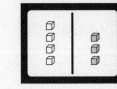

4. Algebra Write the missing number in the addition sentence.

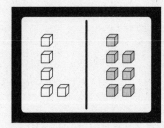

___ + 7 = 12

Stories About Joining

Follow the steps to solve this
joining story.

You have 6 red crayons.
Your teacher gives you 3 blue crayons.
How many crayons do you have in all?

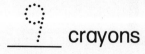

___9___ crayons

Write a number sentence for the story.

___6___ + ___3___ = ___9___

> 1. Draw 6 red crayons in the box.
> 2. Draw 3 blue crayons.
> 3. Count the crayons.

Draw a picture to solve each story problem.
Write a number sentence to go with each story.

1. There are 7 black cats
   in the yard. 3 striped cats
   join them. How many cats
   are there in all?

2. You have 5 stickers.
   Your friend gives you 6 more
   stickers. How many stickers
   do you have in all?

_____ + _____ = _____

_____ + _____ = _____

Stories About Joining

Draw a picture to find the sum.
Then write an addition sentence.

1. The monkey has 2 bananas.
He picks 9 more bananas.
How many bananas does
he have in all?

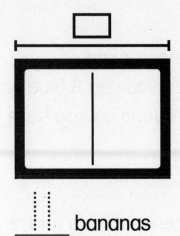

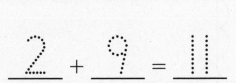

___**2**___ + ___**9**___ = ___**11**___   ___**11**___ bananas

2. Morgan has 3 pennies.
She finds 8 more pennies.
How many pennies does
she have in all?

___ + ___ = ___   ____ pennies

3. Chad has 8 berries on his
pancake. 7 more berries
are in the bowl. How many
berries are there in all?

   Ⓐ 8 berries

   Ⓑ 10 berries

   Ⓒ 15 berries

   Ⓓ 18 berries

4. Reasoning Write a joining
story about the apples.
Use pictures, numbers,
or words.

Writing Subtraction Number Sentences

Count all the cubes. How many?

Now count the cubes with Xs.
How many cubes have Xs?

How many cubes are left?

Count the cubes.
Write a subtraction sentence.

1. _____ − _____ = _____   2. _____ − _____ = _____

3. _____ − _____ = _____   4. _____ − _____ = _____

5. _____ − _____ = _____   6. _____ − _____ = _____

7. _____ − _____ = _____   8. _____ − _____ = _____

Writing Subtraction Number Sentences

Draw the missing part. Write a subtraction sentence.

1. [7]

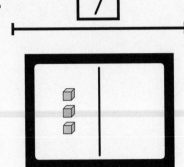

$\underline{7} - \underline{3} = \underline{}$

2. [9]

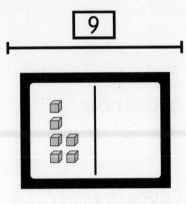

$\underline{} - \underline{} = \underline{}$

3. Kendra had 13 pencils. She took 4 pencils to school. Which subtraction sentence shows how many pencils Kendra left at home?

(A) $17 - 4 = 13$

(B) $13 - 4 = 9$

(C) $13 - 9 = 4$

(D) $9 - 4 = 5$

4. **Spatial Thinking** Draw a picture to show the story. Write a subtraction sentence.

14 mice are outside. Then 7 mice go back in the den. How many mice are still outside?

$\underline{} - \underline{} = \underline{}$

_____ mice

Stories About Separating

6 puppies are playing.
4 run away.
How many puppies are left?

$\underline{6} - \underline{4} = \underline{2}$

Separate a group from the whole.
Then write a subtraction sentence.

1. There are 7 trucks in a lot.
   5 trucks drive away.
   How many trucks are left?

   _____ – _____ = _____

2. There are 8 apples.
   You eat 3 apples.
   How many apples are left?

   _____ – _____ = _____

3. **Journal** Write a separating story about cats.
   Use pictures, numbers, or words. Show
   the answer.

   _____

   _____

   _____

Stories About Separating

Draw a picture to find the difference.
Write a subtraction sentence.

1. Pete has 16 stickers. He uses
9 of them. How many stickers
does he have left?

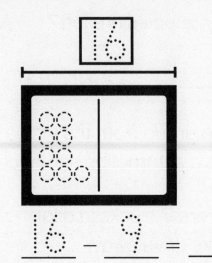

___7___ stickers

_16_ – _9_ = ___

2. Hong has 10 stamps. She
gives 6 stamps to Joe.
How many stamps does
she have left?

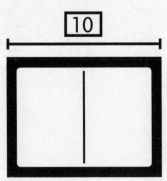

Ⓐ 4 stamps

Ⓑ 5 stamps

Ⓒ 6 stamps

Ⓓ 7 stamps

3. **Reasonableness** James
has 12 rocks. He puts 7 rocks
in Maria's garden. Which
subtraction sentence tells how
many rocks he has left?

Ⓐ 7 – 2 = 5

Ⓑ 7 – 4 = 3

Ⓒ 12 – 5 = 7

Ⓓ 12 – 7 = 5

© Pearson Education, Inc. 2

Stories About Comparing

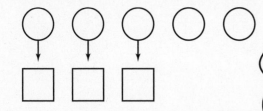

There are __5__ circles.

There are __3__ squares.

> To compare the number of circles and squares, match each circle with a square. Are there more or fewer circles than squares?

How many *more* circles than squares? __2__

__5__ − __3__ = __2__

Draw a picture for each story.
Compare the pictures.
Write a subtraction sentence.

1. There are 6 flowers.
   There are 3 bees.
   How many *more* flowers
   than bees?

   _____ more flowers   ____ − ____ = ____

2. I have 7 juice boxes.
   I have 5 straws.
   How many *fewer* straws
   than juice boxes?

   _____ fewer straws   ____ − ____ = ____

Stories About Comparing

Draw a picture to find the difference.
Write a subtraction sentence.

1. A pond has 11 weeds and
7 lily pads. How many
more weeds than lily pads
does the pond have?

   __4__ more weeds

   11 – 7 = 4

2. A vine has 8 red leaves and
5 brown leaves. How many
fewer brown leaves does
the vine have?

   _____ fewer brown leaves

   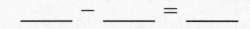
   _____ – _____ = _____

3. Mike plants 6 trees. Faye plants 4 trees.
How many fewer trees does Faye plant than Mike?

   (A) 2 fewer trees

   (B) 4 fewer trees

   (C) 6 fewer trees

   (D) 10 fewer trees

4. **Journal** Write a math story about
comparing to go with the picture.

   _____

   _____

Connecting Addition and Subtraction

Finish the model.
Draw 6 dots to make one part.
Draw 3 dots to make the other part.

Show how the parts make the whole.
Write an addition sentence.

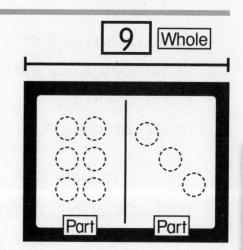

$\dfrac{6}{\boxed{Part}} + \dfrac{3}{\boxed{Part}} = \dfrac{9}{\boxed{Whole}}$

Write subtractions sentences.

$9 - \dfrac{3}{\boxed{Whole}\ \boxed{Part}} = \dfrac{6}{\boxed{Part}}$

$9 - \dfrac{6}{\boxed{Whole}\ \boxed{Part}} = \dfrac{3}{\boxed{Part}}$

Use the addition fact to help.
The addition sentence tells
the parts and the whole.

---

1. Add the parts to this model.
Draw 7 dots and 5 dots.

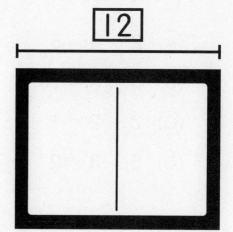

2. Write number sentences for the model.

____ + ____ = ____

____ − ____ = ____

____ − ____ = ____

Connecting Addition and Subtraction

1. Write three number sentences about the shirts. Fill in the model to help you.

   Tim has 5 white shirts. He has 9 colored shirts.

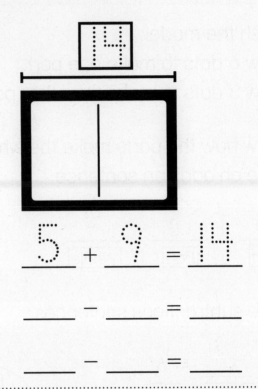

$$5 + 9 = 14$$

___ − ___ = ___

___ − ___ = ___

2. Connie has 2 pairs of jeans. She gets 3 more pairs of jeans.

   Which number sentence shows the story?

   Ⓐ $2 + 3 = 5$

   Ⓑ $5 + 5 = 10$

   Ⓒ $3 - 2 = 1$

   Ⓓ $5 - 3 = 2$

3. **Number Sense** Sarah had 5 caps. She lost 1 cap.

   Which number sentence shows the story?

   Ⓐ $5 + 1 = 6$

   Ⓑ $1 + 6 = 7$

   Ⓒ $6 - 5 = 1$

   Ⓓ $5 - 1 = 4$

Problem Solving: Use Objects

You can use counters and your workmat
to solve this story problem.

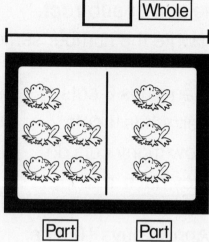

5 frogs are on a rock.
3 frogs join them.
How many frogs in all?

You need to find how many in all,
or the whole.

Show 5 counters.
Show 3 more counters.
How many in all?

Do I need to add or subtract?
I will **add** because I need to
find how many in all.

5 ⊕ 3 = 8
Part   Part   Whole

Use counters and your workmat to solve.
Circle add or subtract. Then write the number sentence.

1. 2 bugs are on a leaf.
   4 bugs join them.
   How many bugs in all?

   add or subtract?

2. 10 toads are in a pond.
   5 toads jump out.
   How many toads are left?

   add or subtract?

   ____ ◯ ____ = ____

Problem Solving: Use Objects

Use counters and a workmat.
Circle **add** or **subtract**.
Then write the number sentence.

1. Sierra has 3 cats.
   Perry has 4 cats.
   How many cats do
   they have in all?

    add   subtract

   3 4 7 cats

---

2. Annika buys 10 gifts.
   Leroy buys 7 gifts.

   Which number sentence
   shows how many more gifts
   Annika buys than Leroy?

   (A) $10 - 7 = 3$

   (B) $10 - 3 = 7$

   (C) $7 + 3 = 10$

   (D) $7 + 7 = 14$

3. 6 friends are playing a game.
   Then 4 friends go home.

   Which number sentence
   shows how many friends are
   playing now?

   (A) $6 + 4 = 10$

   (B) $4 + 2 = 6$

   (C) $10 - 6 = 4$

   (D) $6 - 4 = 2$

---

4. **Journal** Write a math story. Then write a number
   sentence to solve it.

   _____

   _____

Adding 0, 1, 2

You can use a number line to add 0, 1, and 2.

Find 4 on the number line.
0 more than 4 is 4.

$4 + 0 = \underline{4}$

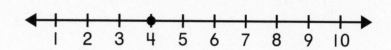

1 more than 4 is 5.

$4 + 1 = \underline{5}$

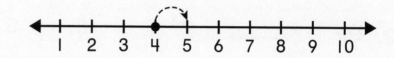

2 more than 4 is 6.

$4 + 2 = \underline{6}$

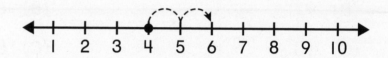

Add 0, 1, and 2.
Use the number line to help you.

1. $5 + 0 = \underline{}$

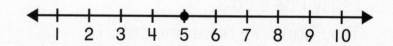

$5 + 1 = \underline{}$

$5 + 2 = \underline{}$

2. $7 + 0 = \underline{}$

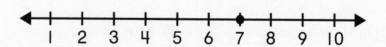

$7 + 1 = \underline{}$

$7 + 2 = \underline{}$

Adding 0, 1, 2

Circle the 0, 1, or 2. Then add.

1. 4
    +②
    6

2. 1
    + 6

3. 7
    + 2

4. 0
    + 8

5. 1 + 8 = _____

6. 0 + 5 = _____

7. 2 + 8 = _____

Ⓐ 8

Ⓑ 9

Ⓒ 10

Ⓓ 11

8. 1 + 3 = _____

Ⓐ 7

Ⓑ 6

Ⓒ 5

Ⓓ 4

9. Solve. Write a number sentence.

Emily has 4 cats.
Troy does not have any cats.
How many cats do Emily
and Troy have in all?

_____ + _____ = _____

They have _____ cats in all.

Number Sense Add.

10. 4 + 0 = _____   0 + 6 = _____   5 + 0 = _____

11. What pattern do you notice in your answers?

_____

12. Use your pattern to find these sums.

17 + 0 = _____   0 + 89 = _____   253 + 0 = _____

Doubles

Find 3 + 3.

Draw 3 more dots to show the double.
Then write the addition sentence.

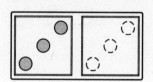

3 + 3 = 6 is a **doubles fact**.

___3___ + ___3___ = ___6___

Draw dots on the domino to show the double.
Then write the addition sentence.

1.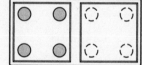

4 + __4__ = __8__

2.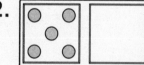

5 + ____ = ____

3.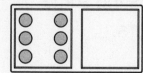

____ + ____ = ____

4.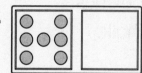

____ + ____ = ____

5.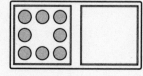

____ + ____ = ____

6.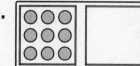

____ + ____ = ____

Doubles

Complete the doubles.
Then solve.

1.
$$\begin{array}{r} 4 \\ + \boxed{4} \\ \hline \vdots 8 \end{array}$$

2.
$$\begin{array}{r} \boxed{} \\ + \ 6 \\ \hline \end{array}$$

3.
$$\begin{array}{r} 2 \\ + \boxed{} \\ \hline \end{array}$$

4.
$$\begin{array}{r} \boxed{} \\ + \ 9 \\ \hline \end{array}$$

5. $8 + \boxed{} =$ _____

6. $\boxed{} + 5 =$ _____

7. $3 + 3 =$ _____

(A) 8

(B) 7

(C) 6

(D) 5

8. $7 + 7 =$ _____

(A) 10

(B) 11

(C) 12

(D) 14

9. Juana has two boxes of chalk. Each box has 8 pieces of chalk.

Which addition fact shows the problem?

(A) $4 + 4 = 8$

(B) $8 + 0 = 8$

(C) $7 + 9 = 16$

(D) $8 + 8 = 16$

10. **Reasoning** Jim has 6 toy cars. Carl has the same number of cars.

How many cars does Carl have?

(A) 6

(B) 10

(C) 12

(D) 16

Near Doubles

You can use a doubles fact to solve a near doubles fact.

To solve a near
doubles fact, add
1 more to the
doubles fact.

$6 + 6 = 12$

Doubles Fact

$6 + 7 = 13$

Near Doubles Fact

1. Write and solve the doubles facts and the
near doubles facts.

   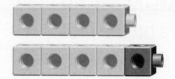

___ + ___ = ___   ___ + ___ = ___

2.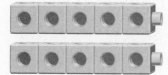

___ + ___ = ___   ___ + ___ = ___

3. **Journal** Draw pictures of cubes to show the facts.
Then solve.

$7 + 7 =$ ____
Doubles Fact

$7 + 8 =$ ____
Near Doubles Fact

Near Doubles

Add. Use the doubles facts to help you.

I. 4   4
  + 4   + 5
    8

2. 6   6
  + 6   + 7

3. 8 + 8 = _____   8 + 9 = _____

4. Solve.

Terry's doll house has 7 windows on the first floor and 8 windows on the second floor.

Which number sentence shows how many windows in all?

(A) 7 + 1 = 8

(B) 7 + 7 = 14

(C) 7 + 8 = 15

(D) 8 + 8 = 16

5. Spatial Thinking Draw a picture to show the story. Then write an addition sentence for the story.

Jane has 5 books.
Fred has 6 books.

How many books in all?

_____ + _____ = _____

_____ books

Adding in Any Order

You can add two numbers in any order.
The answer is the same.

$5 + 2 =$ __7__ $2 + 5 =$ __7__

$5 + 2 = 7$ and $2 + 5 = 7$ are turn-around facts.

Write number sentences for each picture.
Solve the turn-around facts.

1.

____ + ____ = ____   ____ + ____ = ____

2.

____ + ____ = ____   ____ + ____ = ____

3.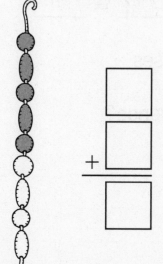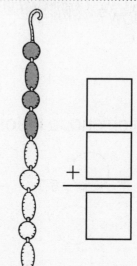

Adding in Any Order

Write the sum. Then write the turn-around fact.

1. $4 + 6 =$ __10__

__6__ + __4__ = __10__

2. $5 + 3 =$ ____

____ + ____ = ____

3. $9 + 4 =$ ____

____ + ____ = ____

4. $2 + 5 =$ ____

____ + ____ = ____

5.

$$\begin{array}{r} 3 \\ + 6 \\ \hline \end{array}$$

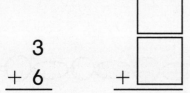

6.

$$\begin{array}{r} 1 \\ + 9 \\ \hline \end{array}$$

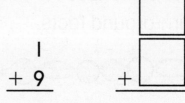

Solve. Write two turn-around facts.

7. A farm has 7 horses.
It gets 2 more horses.
How many horses does
the farm have now?

____ + ____ = ____

____ + ____ = ____

____ horses

8. Geometry Which shape belongs in the sentence?

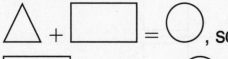

Adding Three Numbers

There are different ways to add three numbers.

You can add any two numbers or try to make 10.
You can also look for doubles or near doubles.
Then add the third number.

Add any 2 numbers.	Try to make 10.	Look for doubles.

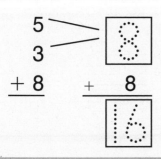

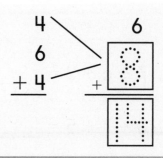

Find the sums.
Draw lines from the first two numbers you add.

I. 7
    4
+ 3

   4
+ ☐

2. 8
    2
+ 5

  ☐
+ 5

3. 1
    6
+ 9

   6
+ ☐

4. 7
    7
+ 5

  ☐
+ 5

5. 8
    4
+ 8

   4
+ ☐

6. 2
    6
+ 7

   2
+ ☐

7. Journal Use pictures, numbers, or words to show
two different ways to add 2 + 4 + 6.

Adding Three Numbers

Write the sum.
Circle the numbers you added first.

Practice 2-5

1. 4
        3
      + 2

2. 6
        0
      + 5

3. 2
        9
      + 2

4. 7
        4
      + 1

5. 7 + 6 + 3 = _____

6. 5 + 0 + 6 = _____

7. 3 + 7 + 5 = _____

Ⓐ 10
Ⓑ 14
Ⓒ 15
Ⓓ 16

8. 3 + 8 + 2 = _____

Ⓐ 13
Ⓑ 12
Ⓒ 11
Ⓓ 10

9. Lila cut out 3 rainbows.
She cut out 4 moons.
She cut out 7 stars.
How many shapes did
Lila cut out in all?

Ⓐ 7
Ⓑ 10
Ⓒ 11
Ⓓ 14

10. Algebra Add across and
down. Write the missing
numbers.

9	3	2	14
	6		14
1		8	14
14	14	14	

Making 10 to Add 9

This shows 9 + 4.

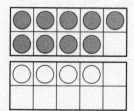

9 + 4 is the same as 10 + 3.

9 + 4 = $\underline{13}$

Show 10 + 3.
Move a counter to make 10.

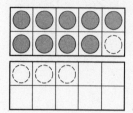

10 + 3 = $\underline{13}$

Make 10 to help you add.

1. Find 9 + 7.

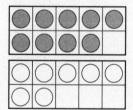

9 + 7 is the same as 10 + 6.

____ + ____ = ____

Move a counter to make 10.

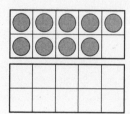

____ + ____ = ____

2. Find 9 + 8.

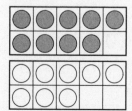

9 + 8 is the same as 10 + 7.

____ + ____ = ____

Move a counter to make 10.

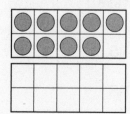

____ + ____ = ____

Making 10 to Add 9

Make 10 to add 9.
Use counters and your workmat.

1. 9
   + 1
   ‾‾‾‾
   10

2. 5
   + 9
   ‾‾‾‾

3. 2
   + 9
   ‾‾‾‾

4. 9
   + 7
   ‾‾‾‾

5. $9 + 4 =$ _____

6. $9 + 8 =$ _____

7. $3 + 9 =$ _____

Ⓐ 11

Ⓑ 12

Ⓒ 13

Ⓓ 14

8. $6 + 9 =$ _____

Ⓐ 15

Ⓑ 16

Ⓒ 17

Ⓓ 18

9. A mother robin pulls
9 worms from a garden.
A father robin pulls
6 worms from a garden.
How many worms do
they have in all?

Ⓐ 18 worms

Ⓑ 17 worms

Ⓒ 15 worms

Ⓓ 14 worms

10. **Number Sense** Write the
missing numbers.

$\underline{7} + \underline{9} = \underline{10} + \underline{6}$

$9 +$ _____ $= 10 + 3$

_____ $+ 9 = 10 + 2$

$9 + 5 = 10 +$ _____

Making 10 to Add 8

This shows 8 + 4.

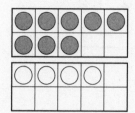

8 + 4 is the same as 10 + 2.

8 + 4 = 12

Show 10 + 2.
Move 2 counters to make 10.

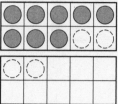

10 + 2 = 12

Make 10 to help you add.

1. Find 8 + 5.

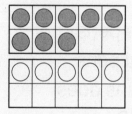

8 + 5 is the same as 10 + 3.

____ + ____ = ____

Move 2 counters to make 10.

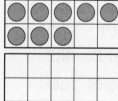

____ + ____ = ____

2. Find 8 + 7.

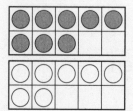

8 + 7 is the same as 10 + 5.

____ + ____ = ____

Move 2 counters to make 10.

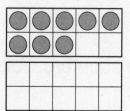

____ + ____ = ____

Making 10 to Add 8

Make 10 to add 8.
Use counters and your workmat.

1. 8
   + 3
   _____

2. 5
   + 8
   _____

3. 8
   + 9
   _____

4. 8
   + 7
   _____

5. 8
   + 1
   _____

6. 4
   + 8
   _____

7. 2
   + 8
   _____

8. 0
   + 8
   _____

9. $6 + 8 =$ _____

10. $8 + 8 =$ _____

11. Jay has 6 yellow blocks.
    He has 8 green blocks.
    How many blocks does
    Jay have in all?

    (A) 13 blocks

    (B) 14 blocks

    (C) 15 blocks

    (D) 16 blocks

12. Tia has 8 blue pens.
    She has 4 red pens.
    How many pens does
    Tia have in all?

    (A) 15 pens

    (B) 14 pens

    (C) 13 pens

    (D) 12 pens

13. **Journal** Use counters. Tell how to make 10 when
    adding $8 + 5$.

    _____

    _____

Problem Solving: Draw a Picture and Write a Number Sentence

Tim and Rose played two games. How many points in all did Tim and Rosa score in Game 1?

Players	Game 1	Game 2
Tim	////	//
Rosa	/////	///// /

Use a part-part-whole mat to find out.

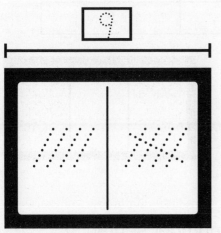

Write a number sentence.

$$\underset{\text{Tim}}{4} + \underset{\text{Rosa}}{5} = \underset{\text{Points in all}}{9}$$

In game 1, Tim and Rosa scored __9__ points in all.

Use a part-part-whole mat and write a number sentence to solve.

1. How many points in all did Tim and Rosa score in Game 2?

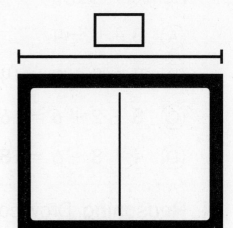

2. _____ + _____ = _____
   Tim   Rosa   Points in all

3. In game 2, Tim and Rosa scored _____ points in all.

Problem Solving: Draw a Picture and Write a Number Sentence

Three children made a table to show how many stickers they have.

Stickers Collected			
	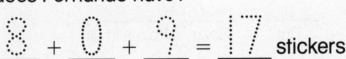 ☺	🌈	🐕
Fernando	8	0	9
Kathleen	4	8	6
Mohammed	5	7	3

1. Draw counters and write a number sentence to solve. How many stickers does Fernando have?

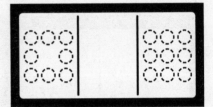

__8__ + __0__ + __9__ = __17__ stickers

2. Which number sentence tells how many stickers Kathleen has?

Ⓐ 8 − 4 = 4

Ⓑ 4 + 8 + 2 = 14

Ⓒ 8 + 2 + 6 = 16

Ⓓ 4 + 8 + 6 = 18

3. Which number sentence tells how many stickers Mohammed has?

Ⓐ 5 + 7 = 12

Ⓑ 7 + 7 + 7 = 21

Ⓒ 5 + 7 + 3 = 15

Ⓓ 5 + 7 + 6 = 18

4. **Reasoning** Draw counters and write a number sentence to show how many 🐕 the children have in all.

____ + ____ + ____ = ____

© Pearson Education, Inc. 2

Name _____

Name _____

Subtracting 0, 1, 2

You can use a number line to subtract 0, 1, and 2.

Find 6 on the number line.
0 less than 6 is 6.

6 − 0 = __6__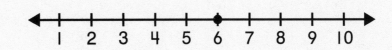

1 less than 6 is 5.

6 − 1 = __5__

2 less than 6 is 4.

6 − 2 = __4__

Subtract 0, 1, and 2.
Use the number line to help you.

1. 4 − 0 = ____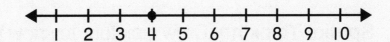

   4 − 1 = ____

   4 − 2 = ____

2. 7 − 0 = ____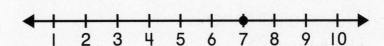

   7 − 1 = ____

   7 − 2 = ____

Subtracting 0, 1, 2

Solve. Use cubes if needed.

1.   7
   − 2

2.   5
   − 1

3.   2
   − 0

4.   1
   − 1

5. 4 − 0 = _____

6.   10 − 2 = _____

7. Kim has 5 teddy bears.
Jill has 1 less teddy bear than Kim.
How many teddy bears does Jill have?

(A) 3

(B) 4

(C) 5

(D) 6

8. **Spatial Thinking** Draw a picture to show the story.
Write a subtraction sentence.

Ted takes a card with
the number 10 on it.
Li takes a card that is
2 less than 10.

What number did Li take?

Li takes the number _____ .   _____ − _____ = _____

Thinking Addition to Subtract Doubles

6 − 3 = ?

Think of a doubles fact.

3 + _3_ = 6

So, 6 − 3 = _3_.

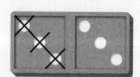

Use doubles facts to help you subtract.

Cross out the dots you take away.

1. 8 − 4 = ?

4 + _4_ = 8   8 − 4 = _4_

2. 10 − 5 = ?

5 + ____ = 10   10 − 5 = ____

3. 12 − 6 = ?

6 + ____ = 12   12 − 6 = ____

4. 14 − 7 = ?

7 + ____ = 14   14 − 7 = ____

5. 16 − 8 = ?

8 + ____ = 16   16 − 8 = ____

6. 18 − 9 = ?

9 + ____ = 18   18 − 9 = ____

Thinking Addition to Subtract Doubles

Subtract. Write the doubles fact that helped you.
Use cubes if you need to.

1.

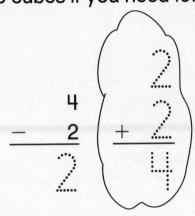

2.

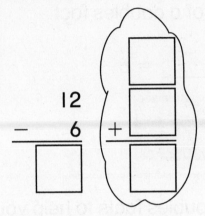

3. $16 - 8 =$ _____

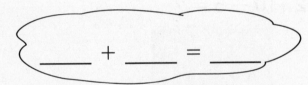

_____ + _____ = _____

4. $18 - 9 =$ _____

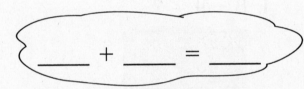

_____ + _____ = _____

5. David had 6 pizzas at his party.
His friends ate 3 pizzas.
Which doubles fact could you use
to find how many pizzas are left?

Ⓐ $3 + 3 = 6$

Ⓑ $6 + 6 = 12$

Ⓒ $6 - 6 = 0$

Ⓓ $6 + 3 = 9$

6. **Reasoning** Krista and Alan have 8 bookmarks.
How could they share the bookmarks so that they
each have the same number?

_____

Thinking Addition to 10 to Subtract

Addition facts can help you subtract.
Use the pictures to find the missing numbers.

Addition Fact	**Subtraction Fact**
	⊗ ⊗
● ● ● ● ● ● ● ●	● ● ● ● ● ● ● ●
Think $2 + \underline{8} = 10$.	So, $10 - 2 = \underline{8}$.

Use addition facts to help you subtract.

1. ○ ○ ○
● ● ● ●

Think $3 + \underline{\hspace{1cm}} = 7$.

⊗ ⊗ ⊗
● ● ● ●

So, $7 - 3 = \underline{\hspace{1cm}}$.

2. ○ ○ ○ ○ ○ ○ ○
●

Think $7 + \underline{\hspace{1cm}} = 8$.

⊗ ⊗ ⊗ ⊗ ⊗ ⊗ ⊗
●

So, $8 - 7 = \underline{\hspace{1cm}}$.

3. ○ ○ ○ ○ ○ ○
● ● ● ●

Think $6 + \underline{\hspace{1cm}} = 10$.

⊗ ⊗ ⊗ ⊗ ⊗ ⊗
● ● ● ●

So, $10 - 6 = \underline{\hspace{1cm}}$.

Thinking Addition to 10 to Subtract

Use addition facts to help you subtract.
Use counters if you need to.

1.

$$\begin{array}{r} 8 \\ -\ 3 \\ \hline 5 \end{array}$$

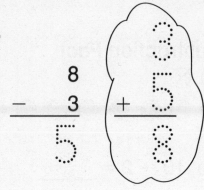

2.

$$\begin{array}{r} 10 \\ -\ 6 \\ \hline \square \end{array}$$

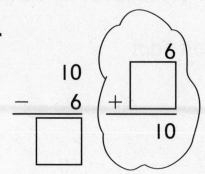

3. $9 - 6 =$ _____

$6 +$ _____ $= 9$

4. $6 - 2 =$ _____

$2 +$ _____ $= 6$

---

5. Number Sense Chris has 7 whistles.
He needs 10 whistles for his party.
Which number sentence can help you find how
many more whistles Chris needs?

Ⓐ $7 + 10 = 17$

Ⓑ $7 - 3 = 4$

Ⓒ $7 + 3 = 10$

Ⓓ $4 + 3 = 7$

Thinking Addition to 18 to Subtract

Addition facts can help you subtract.
Use the pictures to find the missing numbers.

Addition Fact

Think 6 + ___ = 14.

Subtraction Fact

So, 14 − 6 = ___.

Think addition to help you subtract.

1.

Think 9 + ____ = 13.

So, 13 − 9 = ____.

2.

Think 7 + ____ = 15.

So, 15 − 7 = ____.

3.

Think 8 + ____ = 17.

So, 17 − 8 = ____.

4. Algebra Use a related addition fact to complete the subtraction fact.

11 − ____ = 2   2 + ____ = 11

Thinking Addition to 18 to Subtract

Use addition facts to help you subtract.
Use counters if you need to.

1.

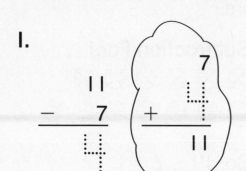

$$\begin{array}{r} 11 \\ -7 \\ \hline 4 \end{array}$$

$$\begin{array}{r} 7 \\ +4 \\ \hline 11 \end{array}$$

2. $15 - 6 =$ _____

$6 +$ _____ $= 15$

---

3. Maria had 11 rings. She lost 3 rings.
Which addition fact can help you find how many
rings Maria has left?

(A) $3 + 1 = 4$

(B) $6 + 5 = 11$

(C) $3 + 8 = 11$

(D) $11 + 3 = 14$

---

4. Journal Write a subtraction story for $12 - 9$.
Then write the addition fact that can help you solve
your story.

_____

_____

_____

____ $+$ ____ $=$ ____ $12 - 9 =$ ____

Finding the Missing Part

Miguel has 3 rocks. He needs 8 rocks.
How many more rocks does he need?

$3 + \boxed{} = 8$

Part   Part   Whole

This addition sentence shows what part is missing.

This is the related subtraction sentence.

$8 - 3 = \boxed{}$

Whole Part   Part

To find the answer, subtract a part from the whole. The whole is always the greater number.

Find the missing parts.

$3 + \underline{5} = 8$

Part   Part   Whole

$8 - 3 = \underline{5}$

Whole Part   Part

Find the missing parts.

1. $5 + \underline{4} = 9$

Part   Part   Whole

$9 - 5 = \underline{4}$

Whole Part   Part

2. $7 + \boxed{} = 10$

$10 - 7 = \boxed{}$

3. $8 + \boxed{} = 15$

$15 - 8 = \boxed{}$

4. $2 + \boxed{} = 8$

$8 - 2 = \boxed{}$

5. Journal Write a story about missing parts.
Use 6 as the whole. Write an addition sentence
and a subtraction sentence to go with your story.

Finding the Missing Part

Find and write the missing numbers.

1. 3 + _____ = 8

   8 − 3 = _____

2. 5 + _____ = 11

   11 − 5 = _____

3. 4 + _____ = 12

   12 − 4 = _____

4. 7 + _____ = 15

   15 − 7 = _____

5. Theo has 5 muffins.
   He needs 14 muffins to serve for breakfast.

   Which problem can help you find
   how many more muffins Theo needs?

   Ⓐ 14 − 5

   Ⓑ 14 + 5

   Ⓒ 5 + 14

   Ⓓ 5 − 14

6. **Algebra** Use the numbers on the cards.
   Write an addition sentence and a subtraction
   sentence.

   _____ + _____ = _____   _____ − _____ = _____

PROBLEM SOLVING
Two-Question Problems

Write the number sentence to solve both parts.

Jenna has 3 red markers and
5 blue markers.
How many markers does she
have in all?

Part 1
Add to find out how many markers
Jenna has in all.

$$3 \bigoplus 5 = 8 \text{ markers}$$

Then Jenna lost 2 markers.
How many markers does
Jenna have left?

Part 2
Subtract the number of markers
Jenna lost.

$$8 \bigominus 2 = 6 \text{ markers}$$

Jenna has ____6____ markers left.

Remember: You have to
solve the first part before you
can solve the second part.

Write the number sentence to solve both parts.

1. There are 5 red apples and
4 green apples in a bowl.
How many apples are in
the bowl?

Part 1

$$\_\_\_\_ \bigoplus \_\_\_\_ = \_\_\_\_ \text{ apples}$$

Ben ate 1 of the apples.
How many apples are in
the bowl now?

Part 2

$$\_\_\_\_ \bigominus \_\_\_\_ = \_\_\_\_ \text{ apples}$$

Problem Solving:
Two-Question Problems

Write the number sentences to solve both parts.

1. Kendra drew 5 pictures. She
threw 2 pictures away. How
many pictures did she keep?

____ ◯ ____ = ____
                   pictures

Then Kendra drew 7 more
pictures. How many pictures
does she have now?

____ ◯ ____ = ____
                   pictures

2. Geometry Troy used a
straw for each side of a
square. How many straws
did he use?

____ straws

If Anita makes 2 squares,
how many straws will she
need?

____ ◯ ____ = ____
                   straws

Mark the number sentences that match the story.

3. Jo buys 2 green cars and
7 red cars. How many cars
does she buy? Then Jo buys
5 yellow cars. How many
cars does she have now?

Ⓐ 5 + 2 = 7 cars
    7 + 5 = 12 cars

Ⓑ 2 + 7 = 9 cars
    9 + 5 = 14 cars

Ⓒ 7 + 2 = 9 cars
    9 − 5 = 4 cars

Ⓓ 7 − 2 = 5 cars
    5 − 5 = 0 cars

4. Reuben checked 9 books
out of the library. He
returned 3 of the books.
How many books does he
have left?

____ ◯ ____ = ____
                   books

Then Reuben returned
3 more books. How many
books does he have now?

____ ◯ ____ = ____
                   books

Models for Tens

Here are 20 ones.

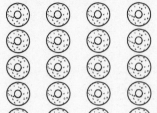

Group the ones
to make 2 tens.

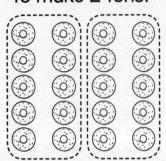

__20__ ones make __2__ tens.

Count the ones. Group the ones to make tens.

1. There are _____ ones.   _____ ones make _____ ten.

---

2. There are _____ ones.   _____ ones make _____ tens.

   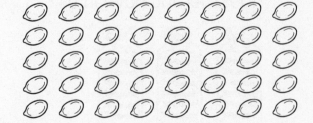

---

3. There are _____ ones.   _____ ones make _____ tens.

   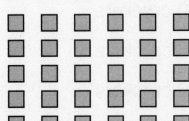

Models for Tens

Write the number of ones.
Draw the tens that you can make.
Write the number of tens.

1.

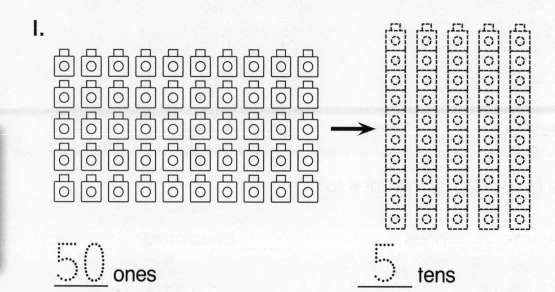

50 ones

___5___ tens

---

2. Serena has these packs of crackers. Each pack has 10 crackers. How many crackers does Serena have in all?

Ⓐ 20 crackers

Ⓑ 30 crackers

Ⓒ 40 crackers

Ⓓ 50 crackers

3. Geometry Which shape would you make if you pushed a cube into the sand?

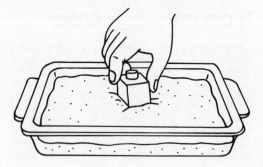

Ⓐ ◯

Ⓑ ▢

Ⓒ ▭

Ⓓ △

Models for Tens and Ones

Ally had 35 raisins to make a snack.
She grouped the raisins into tens and ones.

The raisins on the celery show tens.

The leftover raisins show the ones.

1 ten   1 ten   1 ten   ones

__3__ tens and __5__ ones is __35__.

Count the tens and ones.
Write the numbers.

1.

_____ ten and _____ ones is _____.

2.

_____ tens and _____ ones is _____.

3.

_____ tens and _____ ones is _____.

Models for Tens and Ones

Circle groups of ten.
Tell how many tens and ones.
Write the number.

1.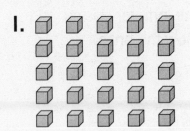

___2___ tens ___5___ ones

___25___

2.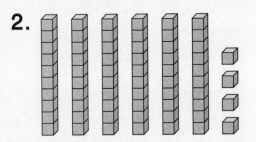

_____ tens _____ ones

_____

3. Sharon cut open this watermelon. How many seeds can you see?

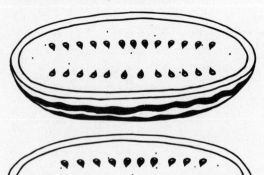

_____ tens _____ ones

_____

4. Estimation Terry has about 20 keys.

Which number could be the exact number of keys that Terry has?

(A) 9

(B) 21

(C) 35

(D) 42

Reading and Writing Numbers

Ones	Teens	Tens
1 one	11 eleven	10 ten
2 two	12 twelve	20 twenty
3 three	13 thirteen	30 thirty
4 four	14 fourteen	40 forty
5 five	15 fifteen	50 fifty
6 six	16 sixteen	60 sixty
7 seven	17 seventeen	70 seventy
8 eight	18 eighteen	80 eighty
9 nine	19 nineteen	90 ninety

Write the number.

7 tens and 8 ones is __78__.

78 has two **digits**.

Write the number word.

seventy and **eight** is

seventy-eight

Write the number and the number word.

1. 2 tens and 9 ones is _____ . _____

2. 6 tens and 3 ones is _____ . _____

3. 9 tens and 2 ones is _____ . _____

4. 8 tens and 6 ones is _____ . _____

Number Sense What is the number?

5. It is greater than 43 and less than 52. If you add the digits, the sum is 8. Write the number word.

_____

6. It is less than 60 and greater than 55. If you add the digits, the sum is 13. Write the number.

_____

Reading and Writing Numbers

Write the number.

1. forty-two 42

2. sixty-five ____

3. fifteen ____

4. fifty-one ____

Write the number word.

5. 33 thirty-three

6. 17 _____

7. 57 _____

8. 26 _____

9. 48 _____

10. 39 _____

11. What number do the cubes show?

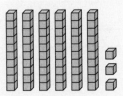

(A) ten

(B) thirty-six

(C) sixty

(D) sixty-three

12. **Number Sense** Write the number word to solve the riddle.

I am greater than 4 tens and less than 5 tens. I have 9 ones. What number am I?

_____

Using Models to Compare Numbers

Compare these numbers.
First compare the tens.

Tens	Ones

Tens	Ones

49 _is greater than_ 35

Compare these numbers.
If the tens are the same, compare the ones.

Tens	Ones

Tens	Ones

24 _is less than_ 25

Use cubes to show the numbers. Write **greater than** or
less than to compare the numbers.

1. 40 is _____ 50

2. 44 is _____ 32

3. 37 is _____ 34

4. 62 is _____ 61

Using Models to Compare Numbers

Write the numbers.
Circle **is greater than** or **is less than**.

1.

    37   is greater than   44

    _____   (is less than)   _____

2.

    is greater than

    _____   is less than   _____

3. Trevor saw 22 monkeys in a picture. He saw 29 birds in the same picture. Did Trevor see more birds or more monkeys?

    more _____

4. Kenya has 18 grapes. She has 21 berries. Does Kenya have more grapes or more berries?

    more _____

5. Laura counted 36 stars. Andy counted more stars than Laura. How many stars could Andy have counted?

    (A) 41 stars

    (B) 35 stars

    (C) 30 stars

    (D) 29 stars

6. **Reasoning** What number am I?

    My tens digit is double my ones digit. I am less than 70 and greater than 60.

    _____

Using Symbols to Compare Numbers

Compare numbers using >, <, and = .

> means "is greater than".
< means "is less than".
= means "equal to".

Tens	Ones
3	4

34 > 32

is greater than

Tens	Ones
3	2

Tens	Ones
3	2

32 < 34

is less than

Tens	Ones
3	4

Tens	Ones
3	2

32 = 32

is equal to

Tens	Ones
3	2

Write less than, greater than, or equal to.
Circle >, <, or = .

1. 13 is _____ 31.

13   >   <   =   31

2. 24 is _____ 24.

24   >   <   =   24

3. 67 is _____ 57.

67   >   <   =   57

4. 63 is _____ 74.

63   >   <   =   74

Using Symbols to Compare Numbers

Write >, <, or = in the ◯.

1. 17 ⊘ 21

2. 59 ◯ 54

3. 29 ◯ 29

4. 12 ◯ 21

5. Solve. Write the numbers. Write <, > or = in the ◯. A toy store has 38 red spiders. It has 43 black spiders. Does it have more red spiders or black spiders?

____ ◯ ____

more _____ spiders

6. A blue jar has 25 marbles. A red jar has 53 marbles. Which shows how to compare the number of marbles?

Ⓐ 25 = 53

Ⓑ 25 > 53

Ⓒ 53 < 25

Ⓓ 53 > 25

7. Journal One box holds 16 crayons. Another box holds 24 crayons. Write a sentence using words that compares the crayons in the two boxes.

_____

_____

_____

Then write a number sentence that compares the two boxes. Use > or <.

____ ◯ ____

Before, After, and Between

1	2	3	4	5	6	7	8	9	10
11	12	13	14	15	16	17	18	19	20
21	22	23	24	25	26	27	28	29	30
31	32	33	34	35	36	37	38	39	40
41	42	43	44	45	46	47	48	49	50
51	52	53	54	55	56	57	58	59	60
61	62	63	64	65	66	67	68	69	70
71	72	73	74	75	76	77	78	79	80
81	82	83	84	85	86	87	88	89	90
91	92	93	94	95	96	97	98	99	100

Use the words **before**, **after**, and **between** to help you find the numbers.

One **before** 66 is 65.

One **after** 66 is 67.

66 is between 65 and 67.

Write the numbers.

1. One before 12 is _____.

   One after 12 is _____.

   The number between

   _____ and _____ is 12.

2. One before 70 is _____.

   One after 70 is _____.

   The number between

   _____ and _____ is 70.

3. One before 45 is _____.

   One after 45 is _____.

   The number between

   _____ and _____ is 45.

4. One before 91 is _____.

   One after 91 is _____.

   The number between

   _____ and _____ is 91.

Before, After, and Between

Write the number that is 1 before, 1 after, or between.
You can use the hundred chart to help.

Before   1. ⌂62⌂, 63   2. _____ , 51

After   3. 39, _____   4. 98, _____

Between   5. 14, _____ , 16   6. 71, _____ , 73

7. The number on the white cap is
1 more than 52 and 1 less than 54.
What number goes on the white cap?

1	2	3	4	5	6	7	8	9	10
11	12	13	14	15	16	17	18	19	20
21	22	23	24	25	26	27	28	29	30
31	32	33	34	35	36	37	38	39	40
41	42	43	44	45	46	47	48	49	50
51	52	53	54	55	56	57	58	59	60
61	62	63	64	65	66	67	68	69	70
71	72	73	74	75	76	77	78	79	80
81	82	83	84	85	86	87	88	89	90
91	92	93	94	95	96	97	98	99	100

(A) 25

(B) 35

(C) 53

(D) 55

8. What number is it?
The number is **after** 45
and **before** 47.

(A) 74

(B) 48

(C) 46

(D) 44

9. Spatial Thinking Which
number comes **10 after**
76 on the hundred chart?

(A) 77

(B) 85

(C) 86

(D) 87

Name _____

Order Numbers

Order 54, 36, and 47 from least to greatest.
Look at the tens first.

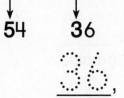

54   36   47

Compare two numbers at a time.

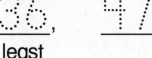

36,   47,   54
least   greatest

Now order 64, 52, and 63 from least to greatest.
If the tens are the same, look at the ones.

64   52   63

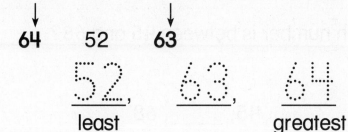

52,   63,   64
least   greatest

Write the numbers in order from least to greatest.

1. 82, 46, 12

_____, _____, _____
least   greatest

2. 32, 61, 22

_____, _____, _____
least   greatest

3. 16, 24, 17

_____, _____, _____
least   greatest

4. 89, 81, 85

_____, _____, _____
least   greatest

5. Journal Draw three racecars with the numbers
25, 18, 77 in order from least to greatest.

Order Numbers

Write the numbers in order from least to greatest.

1. 80, 8, 51

_8_ , _51_ , _80_
least   greatest

2. 24, 32, 16

____ , ____ , ____
least   greatest

3. 96, 78, 87

____ , ____ , ____
least   greatest

4. 44, 64, 62

____ , ____ , ____
least   greatest

5. Reasonableness Which number is between 45 and 68?

(A) 52

(B) 69

(C) 31

(D) 43

45, ____ , 68

6. The chart shows the points that three children earned. Which list shows their points in order from greatest to least?

(A) 21, 34, 17

(B) 17, 21, 34

(C) 17, 34, 21

(D) 34, 21, 17

Spelling Bee Points	
Tommy	21
Paige	34
Kris	17

Number Patterns on the Hundred Chart

1	2	3	4	5	6	7	8	9	10
11	12	13	14	15	16	17	18	19	20
21	22	23	24	25	26	27	28	29	30
31	32	33	34	35	36	37	38	39	40
41	42	43	44	45	46	47	48	49	50
51	52	53	54	55	56	57	58	59	60
61	62	63	64	65	66	67	68	69	70
71	72	73	74	75	76	77	78	79	80
81	82	83	84	85	86	87	88	89	90
91	92	93	94	95	96	97	98	99	100

Look for patterns on the hundred chart.

Start at 10.
Circle skip counts by 10s.

What is the ones digit
in each number?

_____

1. Start at 5.
   Shade skip counts by 5s with a yellow crayon.
   What numbers do you find in the ones digit?

   _____   _____

2. Start at 2.
   Underline skip counts by 2s.
   What numbers do you find in the ones digit?

   _____ _____ _____ _____

3. **Number Sense** Find the pattern.
   Write the next three numbers.

   20, 30, 40, _____, _____, _____

Number Patterns on the Hundred Chart

Finish skip counting.

1	2	3	4	5	6	7	8	9	10
11	12	13	14	15	16	17	18	19	20
21	22	23	24	25	26	27	28	29	30
31	32	33	34	35	36	37	38	39	40
41	42	43	44	45	46	47	48	49	50
51	52	53	54	55	56	57	58	59	60
61	62	63	64	65	66	67	68	69	70
71	72	73	74	75	76	77	78	79	80
81	82	83	84	85	86	87	88	89	90
91	92	93	94	95	96	97	98	99	100

1. Count by 2s.
   Circle each number.

2. Count by 3s.
   Put an X over each number.

3. Which numbers did you circle
   and put an X over?

   _____

   _____

....

Use the hundred chart. Find the pattern.

4. Which car comes next?

   (A)

   (B)

   (C)

   (D)

5. **Algebra** What is the next
   number in this pattern?
   16, 18, 20, _____

   (A) 23

   (B) 22

   (C) 21

   (D) 14

Even and Odd Numbers

An **even** number *can* be shown as two equal parts.
An **odd** number *cannot* be shown as two equal parts.

There are 6 cubes.
Is 6 an even or odd number?
Draw lines to match the cubes.

The cubes can be shown as
two equal parts.

6 is an __even__ number.

There are 7 cubes.
Is 7 an even or odd number?
Draw lines to match the cubes.

The cubes cannot be shown as
two equal parts.

7 is an __odd__ number.

Draw lines to match the cubes.
Is the number even or odd?

1.

10 is an _____ number.

2.

9 is an _____ number.

3.

12 is an _____ number.

4.

15 is an _____ number.

5. Write odd or even. Use cubes to help you.

14 _____   17 _____   20 _____

Even and Odd Numbers

Circle **even** or **odd**. Use cubes if you need to.

1. 24
odd (even)

2. 13
odd   even

3. 52
odd   even

4. 71
odd   even

5. 39
odd   even

6. 47
odd   even

7. 25
odd   even

8. 18
odd   even

9. Draw a picture to solve. Write **even** or **odd**.
Hector has 2 glasses.
He puts 3 ice cubes in one glass
and 2 ice cubes in the other glass.

Does Hector have an odd or even
number of ice cubes?   _____

10. Betty writes a subtraction sentence.
The answer is an even number.
Which subtraction sentence did Betty write?

$8 - 5 = ?$ $7 - 2 = ?$ $9 - 5 = ?$ $6 - 3 = ?$
Ⓐ   Ⓑ   Ⓒ   Ⓓ

11. **Algebra** Use the drawing to answer the questions.

What number do the cubes show? _____

Is the number even or odd? _____

How do you know? _____

_____

PROBLEM SOLVING
Use Data from a Chart

Use clues to find the secret number on the chart.
Cross out numbers on the chart that do not fit each clue.

Clues:

It is greater than 25.

It is less than 30.

It has a 7 in the ones place.

Cross out the numbers 25 and *less*.

11	12	13	14	15	16	17	18	19	20
21	22	23	24	25	26	27	28	29	30
31	32	33	34	35	36	37	38	39	40

Cross out the numbers 30 and *greater*.

Cross out the numbers that don't have a 7 in the ones place. 26, 28, 29

The secret number is __27__.

Use the clues to find the secret number.

31	32	33	34	35	36	37	38	39	40
41	42	43	44	45	46	47	48	49	50
51	52	53	54	55	56	57	58	59	60

It is greater than 40. ⟶ Cross out the numbers _____ and less.

It is less than 46. ⟶ Cross out the numbers _____ and greater.

It has a 5 in the ones place. ⟶ Cross out the numbers

_____.

The secret number is _____.

Use Data from a Chart

Use clues to find the secret number.

Cross out the numbers on the chart that do not fit the clues.

1. The secret number is an even number.
   It is more than 50.
   It has 4 ones.

~~31~~	~~32~~	~~33~~	~~34~~	~~35~~	~~36~~	~~37~~	~~38~~	~~39~~	~~40~~
~~41~~	~~42~~	~~43~~	~~44~~	~~45~~	~~46~~	~~47~~	~~48~~	~~49~~	~~50~~
~~51~~	~~52~~	~~53~~	54	~~55~~	~~56~~	~~57~~	~~58~~	~~59~~	~~60~~

The secret number is __54__.

2. The secret number has a 7 in the ones place.
   The tens number is an odd number.

61	62	63	64	65	66	67	68	69	70
71	72	73	74	75	76	77	78	79	80
81	82	83	84	85	86	87	88	89	90

The secret number is _____.

Use the clues and the chart to solve the problem.

3. **Reasonableness** The flag that Nico waves has an odd number in the ones place and an even number in the tens place.

   What flag does he wave?

   (A) Red Flag

   (B) Blue Flag

   (C) Yellow Flag

   (D) Green Flag

Numbers on Racing Flags	
Red Flag	25
Blue Flag	14
Yellow Flag	32
Green Flag	6
Orange Flag	17

Dime, Nickel, and Penny

| dime
10 cents
10¢
Count dimes by tens. | nickel
5 cents
5¢
Count nickels by fives. | penny
1 cent
1¢
Count pennies by ones. |

10¢   20¢   5¢   10¢   1¢   2¢

Count on to find the total amount. Use coins if you need to.

1. Start with 5¢. Count on by ones.

	Total Amount

5¢   ___   ___   ___   ___

2. Start with 10¢. Count on by fives.

	Total Amount

___   ___   ___   ___   ___

3. Number Sense You have 5 coins that total 23¢.
Label the coins D, N, or P for dimes, nickels, or pennies.

Name _____

Dime, Nickel, and Penny

Count on to find the total amount.

1.

Total Amount
18¢

10¢ 15¢ 16¢ ___ ___

2.

Total Amount

___ ___ ___ ___ ___

3.

Ⓐ 3¢

Ⓑ 15¢

Ⓒ 30¢

Ⓓ 50¢

4.

Ⓐ 4¢

Ⓑ 12¢

Ⓒ 22¢

Ⓓ 40¢

5. Reasoning Draw a picture to solve.
Dara has 5 coins in her purse.
The coins total 40¢.
Draw the coins that Dara has.

Quarter and Half-Dollar

 quarter
25 cents
25¢

 half-dollar
50 cents
50¢

Start with 25¢. Count on by fives.

Think: 25¢ 5¢ more 5¢ more

$\underline{25¢}$ $\underline{30¢}$ $\underline{35¢}$

Start with 50¢. Count on by tens.

Think: 50¢ 10¢ more 10¢ more

$\underline{50¢}$ $\underline{60¢}$ $\underline{70¢}$

Count on to find the total amount.
Use coins if you need to.

1. Start with 25¢. Count on by tens.

Total Amount

$\underline{25¢}$ _____ _____ _____ _____

2. Start with 50¢. Count on by tens and ones.

Total Amount

_____ _____ _____ _____ _____

3. Number Sense Draw coins so the
hand holds 40¢.

Name _____

Quarter and Half-Dollar

Count on to find the total amount.

1.

	Total Amount
25¢ 50¢ 60¢ ____ ____	70¢

2.

	Total Amount
____ ____ ____ ____ ____	

3. Which group of coins has a value of 90¢?

(A)

(B)

(C)

(D)

4. **Reasoning** Jamal has these coins:

He needs 85¢ to buy a toy car.
Draw another coin so that Jamal has
enough money to buy the toy car.

Counting Collections of Coins

To count coins, start with the coin that has the greatest value.

Count on coins from the greatest to the least value.

Find the total amount.

Draw an X on the coin with the greatest value.

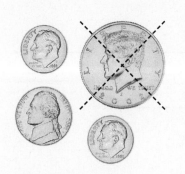

Think: 50¢   60¢   70¢   75¢

Start with 50¢.   50¢ 60¢ 70¢ 75¢

Draw an X on the coin with the greatest value.

Count on to find the total amount.

I.

Start with _____ . _____ _____ _____ _____

2.

Start with _____ . _____ _____ _____ _____

Counting Collections of Coins

Draw the coins from the greatest to the least value.
Count on to find the total amount. You can use coins.

1.

The total amount is ___46¢___.

2.

_____ _____ _____ _____

The total amount is _____.

---

3. Karen has 85 cents.
She has a half dollar and
a dime. Which other coin
does Karen have?

Ⓐ

Ⓑ

Ⓒ

Ⓓ

4. **Estimation** Kobe has about
50¢. Circle the coins he might
have.

Ways to Show the Same Amount

A **dollar bill** is equal to 100¢.

Remember to use a **dollar sign** and **decimal point** when you write $1.00.

100 pennies = **1 dollar**

$100¢ = \$1.00$

Circle coins to show $1.00.
Write the number of coins.

1.

_____ dimes = 1 dollar

2.

quarters = 1 dollar

3.

_____ half-dollars = 1 dollar

4. Algebra What 2 coins will make the statement true?

= $1.00

Ways to Show the Same Amount

Write each total amount.
Circle sets of coins that equal $1.00.

1.

Total Amount
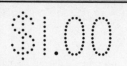

2.

Total Amount

3. Ed has these coins.

How much money does
he need to make a dollar?

Ⓐ 1¢

Ⓑ 5¢

Ⓒ 10¢

Ⓓ 25¢

4. **Number Sense** Pam has
4 coins. The coins total
100¢. Circle the coins
that Pam has.

One Dollar

How much money?

Start counting with the dollar bill.

Then count the coins from the greatest to least value.

Write numbers to show the counting order.

3 _____ 2 _____ 1 _____ 4 _____

Count on to find the total amount.

                 +25   **+10**   **+1**   **$1.36**

$1.00 $1.25 $1.35 $1.36   **Total Amount**

How much money? Count on to find the total amount.

1.     Total Amount

$1.00 $2.00 _____   _____

2.   Total Amount

_____ _____ _____ _____   _____

Name _____

One Dollar

Count on to find the total amount.

1.

			Total Amount
$2	$3	$3.50	$3.50

2.

Total Amount

_____ _____ _____ _____

3.

Total Amount

_____ _____ _____ _____

4. Algebra Abby needs 5 dollars to go to the movie. She has the money shown at the right in her purse. How much money does she need to make 5 dollars?

Ⓐ

Ⓑ

Ⓒ

Ⓓ

Problem Solving:
Make an Organized List

How many ways can you make 25¢?
Two ways are shown in the chart.

Use coins to help you find another way.
Show 1 dime. Make 1 tally mark.

How many nickels do you need to make 15¢?

3
_____

Make 3 tally marks.

Ways to Show 25¢			
Quarter	Dime	Nickel	Total Amount
/			25¢
	/ /	/	25¢
	/	/ / /	25¢

Show 3 ways to make 45¢.
Use tally marks (/) to record the coins.

Ways to Show 45¢			
Quarter	Dime	Nickel	Total Amount
			45¢
			45¢
			45¢

Problem Solving: Make an Organized List

Use coins. Finish the list.

1. Adrian wants to buy a plum for 80¢. He has half dollars, quarters, and dimes. Find all the ways he can make 80¢.

Half Dollar	Quarter	Dime	Total Amount
/		/ / /	80¢
			80¢
			80¢

2. Beth wants to buy some crackers for 23¢. She has dimes, nickels, and pennies. Find four ways she can make 23¢.

Dime	Nickel	Penny	Total Amount
//		///	23¢
			23¢
	////		23¢
			23¢

3. How many ways can Adrian make 80¢?

- (A) 1 way
- (B) 2 ways
- (C) 3 ways
- (D) 4 ways

4. Which coins would Beth use to pay for the crackers with the fewest number of coins?

- (A) dimes and nickels
- (B) nickels and pennies
- (C) pennies
- (D) dimes and pennies

5. Reasonableness Circle **yes** or **no**.
Can you make 38¢ with these coins?

         yes   no

Adding Tens

To add tens, count on by tens.

Add: 35 and 20

> When you add tens, only the digit in the tens place changes.

> Think: Count on 2 tens.

35, __45__, __55__

So, 35 + 20 = __55__.

Add tens. Use cubes or mental math.

1.

46   and   30 = ___

Count on 3 tens:

46, ___, ___, ___

46 + 30 = ___

2.

34   and   50 = ___

Count on 5 tens:

34, ___, ___, ___, ___, ___

34 + 50 = ___

3.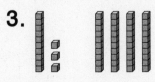

13 and 40 = ___

Count on 4 tens:

13, ___, ___, ___, ___

13 + 40 = ___

Adding Tens

Add using mental math.

1. $20 + 42 =$ **62**

2. $53 + 30 =$ ____

3. $50 + 19 =$ ____

4. $35 + 40 =$ ____

5. $36 + 10 =$ ____

47	46	40	37
Ⓐ	Ⓑ	Ⓒ	Ⓓ

6. $21 + 40 =$ ____

29	41	60	61
Ⓐ	Ⓑ	Ⓒ	Ⓓ

7. Nellie had 14 rubber bands. Then she bought a pack of 30 rubber bands.

How many rubber bands does Nellie have now?

____ rubber bands

8. A squirrel has 26 acorns in its nest. It brings 50 more acorns into the nest.

How many acorns does the squirrel have in all?

____ acorns

9. **Spatial Thinking** Draw tens and ones to solve.

$69 + 20 =$ ____

Adding Ones

36 + 7 = _____

Circle the ones to make the next ten.

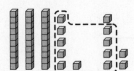

Think: 6 and 4 more make 10.
40 and 3 more make 43.

So, 36 + 7 = **43**

Circle the ones to make the next ten.
Add the ones to the tens.

1.

    28 + 4 = _____

2.
    47 + 8 = _____

3.
    55 + 7 = _____

4.
    36 + 8 = _____

5.

    49 + 6 = _____

6.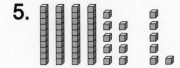

    66 + 8 = _____

Adding Ones

Add the ones. Use mental math.

1. $17 + 4 = $ **21**

2. $38 + 5 = $ _____

3. $49 + 3 = $ _____

4. $23 + 2 = $ _____

5. $65 + 7 = $ _____

6. $52 + 8 = $ _____

7. $38 + 9 = $ _____

47	41	31	17
Ⓐ	Ⓑ	Ⓒ	Ⓓ

8. $65 + 6 = $ _____

11	59	61	71
Ⓐ	Ⓑ	Ⓒ	Ⓓ

9. Janna made a necklace using 18 beads.

Leah made a necklace using only 9 beads.

How many beads did the girls use in all?

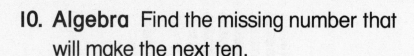

_____ beads

10. **Algebra** Find the missing number that will make the next ten.

$53 + $ _____ $= 60$

6	7	8	9
Ⓐ	Ⓑ	Ⓒ	Ⓓ

Adding Tens and Ones

Find 25 + 34.

25 and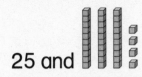

First, count on by tens to add the tens:

> Think: 25 and 3 tens

> Then add the ones.

25, 35, 45, 55

55 and 4 ones is 59.

So, 25 + 34 = 59.

Add. Use mental math or cubes.

1. 34 + 23

34 and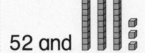

34, _____, _____

54 and _____ ones is _____.

So, 34 + 23 = _____.

2. 52 + 33

52 and

52, _____, _____, _____

_____ and _____ ones is _____.

So, 52 + 33 = _____.

3. 42 + 12 = _____

4. 25 + 21 = _____

Adding Tens and Ones

Add using mental math.

1. $41 + 24 = \underline{65}$

2. $53 + 15 = \underline{}$

3. $56 + 33 = \underline{}$

4. $62 + 25 = \underline{}$

5. $43 + 36 = \underline{}$

6. $50 + 25 = \underline{}$

7. $37 + 21 = \underline{}$

8. $17 + 52 = \underline{}$

9. $46 + 32 = \underline{}$

68	70	74	78
Ⓐ	Ⓑ	Ⓒ	Ⓓ

10. $61 + 13 = \underline{}$

78	74	70	63
Ⓐ	Ⓑ	Ⓒ	Ⓓ

11. Tad has 72 seashells. He finds 15 more shells.

How many seashells does Tad have in all?

82	83	87	92
Ⓐ	Ⓑ	Ⓒ	Ⓓ

12. Estimation One bunch has 31 grapes.
Another bunch has 28 grapes.
About how many grapes are there in all?

Ⓐ about 30 grapes Ⓒ about 60 grapes

Ⓑ about 50 grapes Ⓓ about 70 grapes

Adding on a Hundred Chart

Find 16 + 23.

1. Start on square 16.

2. Move down 2 rows to show the tens in **23**.

3. Move 3 squares to the right to show the ones in **23**.

4. Where did you stop? ⋮3⋮9⋮

   So, ⋮16⋮ + ⋮23⋮ = ⋮39⋮

1	2	3	4	5	6	7	8	9	10
11	12	13	14	15	16	17	18	19	20
21	22	23	24	25	26	27	28	29	30
31	32	33	34	35	36	37	38	39	40
41	42	43	44	45	46	47	48	49	50
51	52	53	54	55	56	57	58	59	60
61	62	63	64	65	66	67	68	69	70
71	72	73	74	75	76	77	78	79	80
81	82	83	84	85	86	87	88	89	90
91	92	93	94	95	96	97	98	99	100

Add using the hundred chart.

1. 12 + 11 = _____

2. 31 + 45 = _____

3. 81 + 14 = _____

4. 48 + 51 = _____

5. 24 + 23 = _____

6. 33 + 56 = _____

7. 52 + 15 = _____

8. 15 + 14 = _____

9. Number Sense Write the number of tens in each number.

67 _____ tens   85 _____ tens   94 _____ tens

Adding on a Hundred Chart

Add using the
hundred chart.

1	2	3	4	5	6	7	8	9	10
11	12	13	14	15	16	17	18	19	20
21	22	23	24	25	26	27	28	29	30
31	32	33	34	35	36	37	38	39	40
41	42	43	44	45	46	47	48	49	50
51	52	53	54	55	56	57	58	59	60
61	62	63	64	65	66	67	68	69	70
71	72	73	74	75	76	77	78	79	80
81	82	83	84	85	86	87	88	89	90
91	92	93	94	95	96	97	98	99	100

1. $47 + 31 =$ __78__

2. $18 + 25 =$ ____

3. $28 + 43 =$ ____

4. $37 + 56 =$ ____

5. $35 + 28 =$ ____

65	63	62	60
Ⓐ	Ⓑ	Ⓒ	Ⓓ

6. $64 + 26 =$ ____

80	82	90	92
Ⓐ	Ⓑ	Ⓒ	Ⓓ

7. **Geometry** Choose the shapes that answer the question.
What weights can you put on the scale to make it balance?

Ⓐ cube and cylinder

Ⓒ pyramid and cube

Ⓑ sphere and cube

Ⓓ rectangular prism and pyramid

Problem Solving: Look for a Pattern

Look for a pattern in these rows of buttons.
Draw buttons to finish the pattern.

2

4

6

8
___

The pattern is to add __2__ buttons each time.

Look for a pattern. Solve.

1. Emma is collecting cans for a recycling project. The chart shows how many cans she plans to collect each week. What is the pattern?

   _____ more cans each week

Week 1	10 cans
Week 2	20 cans
Week 3	30 cans
Week 4	? cans
Week 5	? cans

2. What is Emma's goal for week 4 and week 5?

   Week 4: _____   Week 5: _____

3. **Journal** On a separate piece of paper, create a pattern problem for a friend to solve. Draw a picture or write a story problem.

Problem Solving: Look for a Pattern

Finish the pattern. Solve.

1. On Monday, a cook has 65 frozen pizzas. Each day she bakes 10 of the pizzas. Tuesday, she has 55 pizzas left. Wednesday, she has 45 pizzas left. Continue the pattern.

Monday	65
Tuesday	55
Wednesday	45
Thursday	35
Friday	25

What is the pattern?

Ⓐ Add 5.

Ⓑ Add 10.

Ⓒ Subtract 5.

Ⓓ Subtract 10.

2. In Week 1, Cleo picked 2 tomatoes. In Week 2, she picked 7 tomatoes. In Week 3, she picked 12 tomatoes. Continue the pattern.

Week 1	2
Week 2	7
Week 3	12
Week 4	
Week 5	

What is the pattern?

Ⓐ Add 5.

Ⓑ Add 7.

Ⓒ Subtract 5.

Ⓓ Subtract 7.

3. **Journal** Patty made 4 headbands last week. She made 8 this week. Next week, she will make 12. What is the pattern? How many headbands will Patty make the following week?

_____   _____ headbands

Subtracting Tens

Here are two ways you can find 57 − 30.

1. Count back 3 tens, or 30.

57, _47_, _37_, _27_

When you subtract tens, only the tens digit changes.

2. Use cubes to subtract the tens.

50 − 30 = _20_

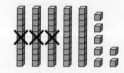

Then subtract the ones.

7 − 0 = _7_

So, 57 − 30 = _27_.

Count back to subtract tens. Use cubes if needed.

1. 64 − 30 =

64, _____, _____, _____

64 − 30 = _____

2. 62 − 40 = _____

3. 76 − 20 = _____

4. 84 − 50 = _____

5. 95 − 70 = _____

Subtracting Tens

Subtract. Use mental math.

1. $76 - 40 = \underline{36}$

2. $98 - 50 = \underline{}$

3. $94 - 60 = \underline{}$

4. $33 - 20 = \underline{}$

5. $65 - 10 = \underline{}$

6. $52 - 30 = \underline{}$

7. $47 - 30 = \underline{}$

Ⓐ 37

Ⓑ 30

Ⓒ 20

Ⓓ 17

8. $61 - 40 = \underline{}$

Ⓐ 20

Ⓑ 21

Ⓒ 30

Ⓓ 41

9. Use mental math to solve.

A box holds 48 crackers. Austin ate 10 of them.

How many crackers are left in the box?

Ⓐ 18

Ⓑ 28

Ⓒ 38

Ⓓ 58

10. Number Sense Allie had 36¢. On Thursday she spent 10¢, and on Friday she spent 10¢ more.

How much money does she have now?

Ⓐ 46¢

Ⓑ 36¢

Ⓒ 26¢

Ⓓ 16¢

Finding Parts of 100

Find parts for 100.

Draw more tens to make 100.

Think: Add on to make 100.

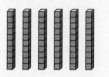

60 and **40** is 100.

60 + **40** = 100

Now draw tens and ones to make 100. Add on.

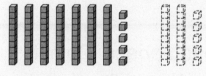

75 and **25** is 100.

75 + **25** = 100

Draw tens to find the other part of 100.

1.

50 and _____ is 100.

50 + _____ = 100

Draw tens and ones to make 100. Add on.

2.

45 and _____ is 100.

45 + _____ = 100

Finding Parts of 100

Add on to find the other part of 100.

1. $54 + \underline{46} = 100$

2. $29 + \underline{\hspace{1cm}} = 100$

3. $43 + \underline{\hspace{1cm}} = 100$

4. $72 + \underline{\hspace{1cm}} = 100$

5. $89 + \underline{\hspace{1cm}} = 100$

6. $18 + \underline{\hspace{1cm}} = 100$

7. $37 + \underline{\hspace{1cm}} = 100$

8. $61 + \underline{\hspace{1cm}} = 100$

9. $65 + \underline{\hspace{1cm}} = 100$

10. $46 + \underline{\hspace{1cm}} = 100$

Solve.

11. Latisha had a box of 100 birthday cards. So far, she has sent out 47 cards.

    How many cards are left in the box?

    Ⓐ 51 cards

    Ⓑ 52 cards

    Ⓒ 53 cards

    Ⓓ 54 cards

12. **Reasonableness** Do not add or subtract. Read each answer. Choose the most reasonable answer.

    A store had 100 class rings. They sold 37 rings. How many are left?

    Ⓐ 63 rings

    Ⓑ 50 rings

    Ⓒ 35 rings

    Ⓓ 10 rings

Subtracting on a Hundred Chart

A hundred chart can help you subtract.

1	2	3	4	5	6	7	8	9	10
11	12	13	14	15	16	17	18	19	20
21	22	23	24	25	26	27	28	29	30
31	32	33	34	35	36	37	38	39	40
41	42	43	44	45	46	47	48	49	50
51	52	53	54	55	56	57	58	59	60
61	62	63	64	65	66	67	68	69	70
71	72	73	74	75	76	77	78	79	80
81	82	83	84	85	86	87	88	89	90
91	92	93	94	95	96	97	98	99	100

Find 36 − 24.

1. Start at 24.

2. Move down to 34.
   This is the row that 36 is in.

   One row down makes __10__.

3. Move right from 34 to 36 to count __2__ ones.

4. Count the tens down and ones across.

   __10__ + __2__ = __12__, so 36 − 24 = 12.

Subtract using the hundred chart.

1. 87 − 72 = ____

2. 79 − 48 = ____

3. 65 − 41 = ____

4. 99 − 52 = ____

5. 35 − 13 = ____

6. 84 − 33 = ____

Subtracting on a Hundred Chart

Subtract using the hundred chart.

1	2	3	4	5	6	7	8	9	10
11	12	13	14	15	16	17	18	19	20
21	22	23	24	25	26	27	28	29	30
31	32	33	34	35	36	37	38	39	40
41	42	43	44	45	46	47	48	49	50
51	52	53	54	55	56	57	58	59	60
61	62	63	64	65	66	67	68	69	70
71	72	73	74	75	76	77	78	79	80
81	82	83	84	85	86	87	88	89	90
91	92	93	94	95	96	97	98	99	100

1. $47 - 31 =$ __16__

2. $78 - 25 =$ ____

3. $99 - 43 =$ ____

4. $37 - 16 =$ ____

5. $55 - 23 =$ ____

6. $64 - 26 =$ ____

7. A pan holds 36 biscuits. Kiana put 12 biscuits on the pan.

How many more biscuits will fit on the pan?

(A) 24 biscuits

(B) 23 biscuits

(C) 22 biscuits

(D) 21 biscuits

8. A garden has room for 22 flowers. Dan needs to plant 11 more flowers.

How many flowers did Dan already plant?

(A) 10 flowers

(B) 11 flowers

(C) 12 flowers

(D) 13 flowers

9. **Journal** Explain how to use a hundred chart to subtract.

_____

_____

Adding On to Subtract

If you have 57 and take away 32, how many are left?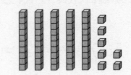

Find 57 − 32.

First, count back by tens to subtract 3 tens.

57, _47_, _37_, _27_

Then, count back to subtract 2 ones.

27, _26_, _25_

So, _57_ − _32_ = _25_

Here is another way to subtract.
First, add 8 cubes to make the next ten, 40.

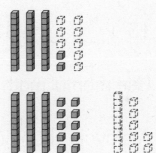

Then, count up from 40 to 57.

Add. 8 + 17 = 25

So, 57 − 32 = _25_

Subtract and add on to find the difference.

1. 23 − 11 = ____

11 + ____ = 23

2. 68 − 34 = ____

34 + ____ = 68

3. Journal Write an addition sentence to go with this
subtraction sentence.
48 − 23 = 25

Adding On to Subtract

Subtract and add on to find the difference.

1. $76 - 42 = \underline{34}$

$42 + \underline{34} = 76$

2. $62 - 41 = \underline{}$

$41 + \underline{} = 62$

3. $58 - 33 = \underline{}$

$33 + \underline{} = 58$

4. $45 - 22 = \underline{}$

$22 + \underline{} = 45$

5. $37 - 15 = \underline{}$

$15 + \underline{} = 37$

6. $26 - 12 = \underline{}$

$12 + \underline{} = 26$

7. Use mental math to solve.

A bicycle shop had 38 bicycles. It sold 24 bikes the first week of June.

How many bicycles are left?

- (A) 4 bicycles
- (B) 14 bicycles
- (C) 24 bicycles
- (D) 28 bicycles

8. Reasoning Use the numbers on the cards to write 2 two-digit numbers that make a difference of 25.

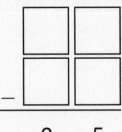

2   5

Problem Solving: Missing or Extra Information

Solve.

There are 4 children
on a bowling team.
Mike bowls a score of 55.
Sherry bowls a score of 30.
How much higher is Mike's score?

> Sometimes you do not have enough information to solve a problem. Sometimes you have too much information and you do not need it to solve a problem.

> 1. What do you need to find out?

The difference between Mike's and Sherry's score.

> 2. What information do you need to solve the problem?

Mike's score and Sherry's score:

$$55 - 30 = 25$$

> 3. What information is extra?

There are 4 children on the team.

Cross out the extra information.
Solve the problem if you have the information you need.

1. There are 39 adults at the bowling alley.
   There are 9 children at the bowling alley.
   ~~Mark bowls a score of 82.~~

   How many more adults than children are there?

   Solve if you can: _____ − _____ = _____

Problem Solving: Missing or Extra Information

Circle **Extra Information** or **Missing Information**.
Then write a number sentence if the problem can be solved.

1. Julia painted 12 pictures and made 3 clay baskets at school. Julia took 5 pictures home. How many pictures are left at school?

(Extra Information)

Missing Information

$12 - 5 = 7$ pictures

2. Nico cut out 15 red circles and 10 yellow circles. Then he gave away some red circles. How many red circles does Nico have left?

Extra Information

Missing Information

_____ − _____ = _____ red circles

Spatial Thinking Draw a picture to solve each problem. Then choose the correct answer.

3. A bush had 18 berries. A raccoon ate 9 of the berries. Then the raccoon ate 6 fish. How many berries are left?

(A) 11 berries
(B) 10 berries
(C) 9 berries
(D) 8 berries

4. A bowl holds 16 oranges and 4 apples. Children eat 9 oranges. How many oranges are left in the bowl?

(A) 7 oranges
(B) 8 oranges
(C) 9 oranges
(D) 10 oranges

Regrouping 10 Ones for 1 Ten

Find the sum.

24 + 8 = _____

Regroup 10 ones as 1 ten.

There are __3__ tens and __2__ ones

24 + 8 = __32__

Tens	Ones

Regroup 10 ones as 1 ten.
Add. Count the tens and the ones.

1.

Tens	Ones

28 + 3 = _____

2.

Tens	Ones

47 + 7 = _____

3.

Tens	Ones

55 + 6 = _____

4.

Tens	Ones

36 + 8 = _____

Regrouping 10 Ones for 1 Ten

Use cubes and a workmat.

Add. Regroup if you need to.

Show.	Add.	Do you need to regroup?		Show.
1. 24	7	(Yes)	No	$24 + 7 =$ 31
2. 56	9	Yes	No	$56 + 9 =$ _____
3. 92	6	Yes	No	$92 + 6 =$ _____

4. Pat had 6 forks. Then she bought a pack of 18 forks. How many forks does she have now?

   (A) 12

   (B) 14

   (C) 24

   (D) 26

5. Theo counted 69 red plates. Then he counted 8 blue plates. How many plates did he count in all?

   (A) 79

   (B) 77

   (C) 71

   (D) 61

6. Spatial Thinking Solve the problem by drawing tens and ones in the place-value chart.

$48 + 5 =$ _____

Tens	Ones

Models to Add Two- and One-Digit Numbers

Add 35 + 7.

Step 1:

How many ones?

5 + 7 = 12

Tens	Ones

	Tens	Ones
	3	5
+		7
		2

Step 2:

Regroup 12 as
1 ten and 2 ones.
Write 2 ones.

Tens	Ones

	Tens	Ones
	1	
	3	5
+		7
		2

Step 3:

How many tens?

3 + 1 = 4 tens

Tens	Ones

	Tens	Ones
	1	
	3	5
+		7
	4	2

So, 35 + 7 = 42.

Use connecting cubes and the workmat. Add.
Did you need to regroup? Circle **yes** or **no**.

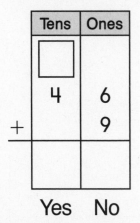

Tens	Ones
4	6
+	9

Yes   No

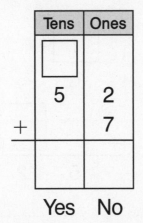

Tens	Ones
5	2
+	7

Yes   No

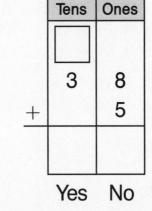

Tens	Ones
3	8
+	5

Yes   No

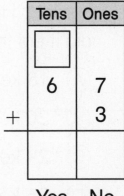

Tens	Ones
6	7
+	3

Yes   No

Models to Add Two- and One-Digit Numbers

Use connecting cubes and a workmat. Add.
Do you need to regroup? Circle **Yes** or **No**.

1.

Tens	Ones
1	
2	8
+	5
3	3

(Yes) No

2.

Tens	Ones
6	4
+	9

Yes No

3.

Tens	Ones
5	2
+	5

Yes No

4.

Tens	Ones
	7
+ 1	9

Yes No

5.

Tens	Ones
2	5
+	7

Yes No

6.

Tens	Ones
4	3
+	8

Yes No

7.

Tens	Ones
5	4
+	2

Yes No

8.

Tens	Ones
3	3
+	7

Yes No

9. A crow ate 22 kernels of corn. Then it ate 4 more kernels. How many kernels did it eat in all?

Ⓐ 18 kernels

Ⓑ 20 kernels

Ⓒ 24 kernels

Ⓓ 26 kernels

10. Algebra Write the missing numbers in the boxes.

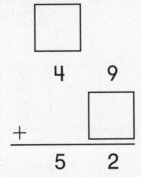

Name _____

Adding Two- and One-Digit Numbers

Remember the steps for adding.

Step 1: Add the ones.

Step 2: Regroup if there are more than 10 ones.

Step 3: Add the tens.

$37 + 6 = ?$

There are more than 10 ones.

Regroup 13 as 1 ten and 3 ones. Add.

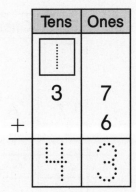

Tens	Ones
1	
3	7
+	6
4	3

Use paper and pencil to add.

1. Do you need to regroup?

Yes   No

Tens	Ones
2	8
+	4

2. Do you need to regroup?

Yes   No

Tens	Ones
3	6
+	9

3. Do you need to regroup?

Yes   No

Tens	Ones
3	4
+	5

4. Do you need to regroup?

Yes   No

Tens	Ones
4	6
+	4

Adding Two- and One-Digit Numbers

Add. Regroup if you need to.

1.

Tens	Ones
7	6
+	7
8	3

2.

Tens	Ones
6	4
+	3

3.

Tens	Ones
8	3
+	6

4.

Tens	Ones
3	7
+	9

5.

Tens	Ones
7	5
+	7

6.

Tens	Ones
5	0
+	8

7.

Tens	Ones
7	6
+	4

8.

Tens	Ones
8	3
+	5

9. Bessie has 25 flowers. Then she picks 9 more flowers. How many flowers does Bessie have in all?

(A) 33

(B) 34

(C) 35

(D) 36

10. Journal Tell how you know when to regroup.

_____

_____

_____

_____

Name _____

Models to Add Two-Digit Numbers

Add 46 + 18.

Step 1:
How many ones?

$6 + 8 = \underline{14}$

Tens	Ones

	Tens	Ones
	4	6
+	1	8
		4

Step 2:
Do I need to regroup?

(yes)   no

Tens	Ones

	Tens	Ones
	1	
	4	6
+	1	8
		4

Step 3:
How many tens?

$5 + 1 = \underline{6}$ tens

Tens	Ones

	Tens	Ones
	1	
	4	6
+	1	8
	6	4

So, $46 + 18 = \underline{64}$.

Follow the steps. Use connecting cubes and the workmat. Add.

	Tens	Ones
	2	4
+	2	9

	Tens	Ones
	5	2
+	1	7

	Tens	Ones
	3	8
+	4	5

	Tens	Ones
	1	7
+	6	3

Models to Add Two-Digit Numbers

Use connecting cubes and the workmat. Add.
Do you need to regroup? Circle **Yes** or **No**.

1.

Tens	Ones
⫶	
3	3
+ 4	9
8	2

(Yes) No

2.

Tens	Ones
☐	
5	1
+ 4	7

Yes No

3.

Tens	Ones
☐	
2	3
+ 3	7

Yes No

4.

Tens	Ones
☐	
4	4
+ 2	8

Yes No

5. Lia counts 38 red paper cups and 25 blue paper cups. How many paper cups did she count in all?

Ⓐ 13

Ⓑ 43

Ⓒ 53

Ⓓ 63

Tens	Ones
☐	
+	

6. Reasonableness Use the clues to solve the riddle.

I am between 24 and 34.

You say my name when you count by twos from zero.

You say my name when you count by fives from zero.

What number am I?

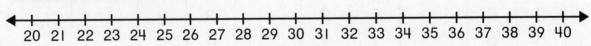

20 21 22 23 24 25 26 27 28 29 30 31 32 33 34 35 36 37 38 39 40

I am the number _____.

Adding Two-Digit Numbers

Remember the steps for adding:

Step 1:
Add the ones.

Step 2:
Regroup if you need to.

Step 3:
Add the tens.

34 + 27 = ?
Regroup 11 ones
as 1 ten and 1 one.

Tens	Ones
[1]	
3	4
+ 2	7
6	1

12 + 36 = ?
You do not
need to regroup
8 ones.

Tens	Ones
1	2
+ 3	6
4	8

Write the addition problem. Find the sum.

1.

15 + 26

Tens	Ones
1	5
+ 2	6

32 + 24

Tens	Ones
3	2
+ 2	

28 + 15

Tens	Ones
2	8
+	

49 + 13

Tens	Ones
4	9
+	

2. **Algebra** Begin with 39. Find the number
that gives you a sum of 56. Use connecting
cubes to help.

The number is _____.

Tens	Ones
3	9
+	
5	6

Adding Two-Digit Numbers

Write the addition problem. Find the sum.

1. 26 + 52

Tens	Ones
□	
2	6
+ 5	2
7	8

2. 31 + 19

Tens	Ones
□	
+	

3. 47 + 28

Tens	Ones
□	
+	

4. 56 + 34

Tens	Ones
□	
+	

5. 63 + 26

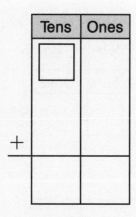

Tens	Ones
□	
+	

6. 75 + 13

Tens	Ones
□	
+	

7. 68 + 29

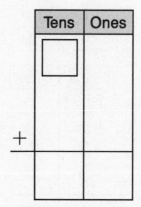

Tens	Ones
□	
+	

8. 54 + 37

Tens	Ones
□	
+	

9. Paul has a stack of 43 pennies and a stack of 36 pennies. How many pennies does he have altogether?

ⓐ 47 pennies

ⓑ 66 pennies

ⓒ 79 pennies

ⓓ 89 pennies

10. Estimation One jar has 38 buttons. Another jar has 43 buttons. About how many buttons are in both jars?

ⓐ about 80 buttons

ⓑ about 70 buttons

ⓒ about 60 buttons

ⓓ about 50 buttons

Adding Three Numbers

You can add three numbers in any order.
Remember to add the ones first.

Look for doubles.

$$
\begin{array}{r}
14 \\
35 \\
+\ 24 \\
\hline
73
\end{array}
$$

$4 + 4 = 8$
$8 + 5 = 13$

Make a ten.

$$
\begin{array}{r}
13 \\
26 \\
+\ 24 \\
\hline
63
\end{array}
$$

$6 + 4 = 10$
$10 + 3 = 13$

Count on.

$$
\begin{array}{r}
53 \\
19 \\
+\ 22 \\
\hline
94
\end{array}
$$

Add 9 and 3.
$9 + 3 = 12$
Count on from 12. 13, 14.

Add. Circle the numbers you add first.

1. Look for doubles.	2. Count on.	3. Make a ten.	4. Choose a way to add.
$\begin{array}{r} 10 \\ 34 \\ +\ 24 \\ \hline \end{array}$	$\begin{array}{r} 12 \\ 17 \\ +\ 24 \\ \hline \end{array}$	$\begin{array}{r} 15 \\ 28 \\ +\ 22 \\ \hline \end{array}$	$\begin{array}{r} 26 \\ 22 \\ +\ 36 \\ \hline \end{array}$

5. Journal Write an addition problem with three numbers.
Solve it. Then have a friend solve it. Compare how
you and your friend add the numbers.

Adding Three Numbers

Add. Circle the two numbers you added first.

1.   34
     19
   + 41

     94

2.   61
     10
   + 26

3.   28
     34
   + 12

4.   19
     26
   + 31

5.   47
     22
   + 24

6.   51
      8
   + 25

7.   72
     16
   + 8

8.   37
     21
   + 16

9. These animals live in a big garden:

   37 snails

   49 worms

   12 moths

   How many animals live in the garden altogether?

   (A) 98

   (B) 97

   (C) 88

   (D) 87

10. **Number Sense** Use the numbers shown. Make the sum of the numbers across equal the sum of the numbers down.

   7   5   1   9   3

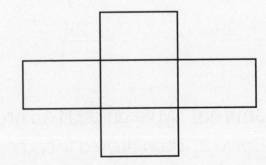

Problem Solving: Draw a Picture and Write a Number Sentence

Look for clue words to help you solve a story problem.

Tina has 23 counters.
She gets 27 more counters.
How many counters does Tina have in all?

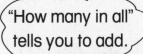
"How many in all" tells you to add.

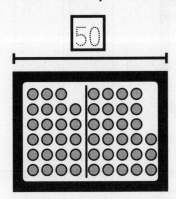

$23 + 27 = 50$

Tens	Ones
1	
2	3
+ 2	7
5	0

Draw pictures to solve the problem.
Then write a number sentence.

1. Raul has 15 counters.
   He gets 19 more counters.
   How many does he have in all?

Tens	Ones
+	

___ + ___ = ___

Problem Solving: Draw a Picture and Write a Number Sentence

Write a number sentence to solve each problem.
Use the part-part-whole mat if needed.

1. Jordan had 19¢. Then he found 17¢ more. How much money does he have now?

   $19 + 17 = 36$ ¢

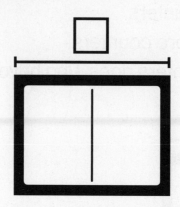

Tens	Ones
+	

2. Cara has 14 toys. Tori has 18 toys. How many toys do the girls have in all?

   ____ + ____ = ____ toys

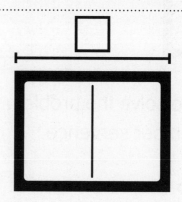

Tens	Ones
+	

3. Curt made paper cranes. He made 45 blue cranes. He made 17 green cranes.

   Which number sentence shows how many paper cranes he made in all?

   (A) $45 - 17 = 28$

   (B) $17 + 17 = 34$

   (C) $45 + 17 = 62$

   (D) $45 + 45 = 90$

4. **Algebra** Which number is missing?

   (A) 4

   (B) 3

   (C) 2

   (D) 1

Tens	Ones
1	
2	8
+ 1	4
?	2

Regrouping 1 Ten for 10 Ones

Subtract 7 from 42.

Show 42.

Tens	Ones

There are not enough ones to subtract 7.

Regroup.

Tens	Ones

1 ten becomes 10 ones.

Subtract 7 ones.

Tens	Ones

Do you need to regroup?

(Yes)   No

$12 - 7 = 5$ ones

$42 - 7 = $ 35

Subtract. Regroup if needed.
Use cubes and a workmat to help.

1. Subtract 5 from 31.

Show 31.

Tens	Ones

Regroup.

Tens	Ones

Subtract  5 ones.

Tens	Ones

Do you need to regroup?

(Yes)   No

$11 - 5 = $ 6 ones.

$31 - 5 = $ ____

Regrouping 1 Ten for 10 Ones

Subtract. Regroup if you need to.
Use cubes and a workmat to help.

Show.	Subtract.	Do you need to regroup?	Find the difference.
1. 47	9	(Yes) No	$47 - 9 = \underline{38}$
2. 52	6	Yes No	$52 - 6 = \underline{\hspace{1cm}}$
3. 38	5	Yes No	$38 - 5 = \underline{\hspace{1cm}}$

4. Use cubes and a workmat to solve the problem.

An old building has 48 windows. 19 of them are broken. How many windows are not broken?

(A) 29 windows

(B) 30 windows

(C) 31 windows

(D) 32 windows

5. **Spatial Thinking** The pole is 30 feet tall. The bug has crawled 14 feet. How much farther does the bug need to crawl to get to the top?

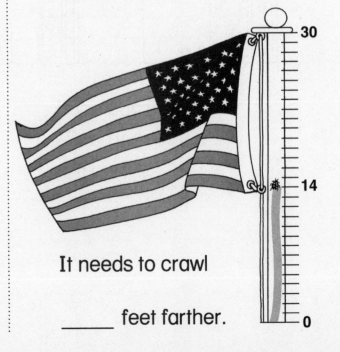

It needs to crawl

_____ feet farther.

© Pearson Education, Inc. 2

Name _____

Models to Subtract Two- and One-Digit Numbers

Subtract 8 from 52.

Step 1	Step 2	Step 3
Think: There are not enough ones to subtract 8.	Regroup 1 ten as 10 ones. Write 12 ones. $12 - 8 = 4$ ones	Subtract the tens. $4 - 0 = 4$ tens

Tens	Ones
5	2
−	8

Tens	Ones
4	12
5	2
−	8
	4

Tens	Ones
4	12
5	2
−	8
4	4

So, $52 - 8 = \underline{44}$.

Subtract. Use cubes and a workmat to help.
Did you need to regroup? Circle **yes** or **no**.

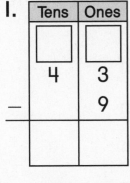

1. | Tens | Ones |
|---|---|
| | |
| 4 | 3 |
| − | 9 |
| | |

yes   no

Tens	Ones
6	9
−	3

yes   no

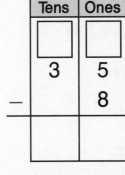

Tens	Ones
3	5
−	8

yes   no

Tens	Ones
7	6
−	7

yes   no

Models to Subtract Two- and One-Digit Numbers

Subtract. Regroup if you need to.
Use cubes and a workmat to help.

1.

Tens	Ones
1	16
2	6
−	7
1	9

2.

Tens	Ones
5	2
−	8

3.

Tens	Ones
7	7
−	5

4.

Tens	Ones
3	9
−	6

5.

Tens	Ones
4	5
−	7

6.

Tens	Ones
6	1
−	7

7.

Tens	Ones
9	0
−	4

8.

Tens	Ones
6	8
−	9

9. Solve.

A bakery makes 64 muffins. They sell 29 muffins by noon. How many muffins are left?

Ⓐ 45 muffins

Ⓑ 44 muffins

Ⓒ 35 muffins

Ⓓ 34 muffins

10. Reasonableness There are 45 children in the gym. Some children leave. How many children could be in the gym now?

Ⓐ 37 children

Ⓑ 45 children

Ⓒ 51 children

Ⓓ 62 children

Name _____

Subtracting Two- and One-Digit Numbers

Remember the steps for subtracting.

Step 1
Think: Are there enough ones to subtract?

Step 2
Regroup the ones if you need to. Subtract.

Step 3
Subtract the tens.

Subtract.
Regroup if you need to.

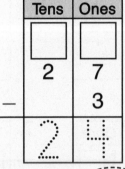

Regroup?   Yes   (No)

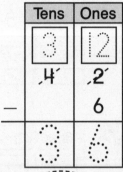

Regroup?   (Yes)   No

Remember the steps for subtracting.
Subtract. Regroup if you need to.

1.

Tens	Ones
2	5
−	4

Tens	Ones
4	1
−	8

Tens	Ones
6	5
−	7

Tens	Ones
7	8
−	9

2. Journal Write a subtraction problem that needs regrouping.

Tens	Ones
−	

Subtracting Two- and One-Digit Numbers

Subtract. Regroup if you need to.

1.

Tens	Ones
6	12
7	2
−	5
6	7

2.

Tens	Ones
6	1
−	7

3.

Tens	Ones
8	3
−	6

4.

Tens	Ones
3	8
−	3

5.

Tens	Ones
7	6
−	2

6.

Tens	Ones
9	3
−	4

7.

Tens	Ones
2	6
−	7

8.

Tens	Ones
8	7
−	8

9. Katara takes 21 kites to the park. She sells 17 of the kites. How many kites are left?

Ⓐ 3 kites

Ⓑ 4 kites

Ⓒ 14 kites

Ⓓ 17 kites

10. Journal Tell how you know when to regroup.

_____

_____

_____

_____

_____

Models to Subtract Two-Digit Numbers

Subtract 16 from 43.

Step 1	Step 2	Step 3
Think: There are not enough ones to subtract 6.	Think: Do I need to regroup?	Think: Subtract the tens.

Step 2: $13 - 6 = \underline{7}$ ones

Step 3: $3 - 1 = \underline{2}$ tens

Step 1

Tens	Ones

Tens	Ones
4	3
− 1	6

Step 2

Tens	Ones

Tens	Ones
3	13
4	3
− 1	6
	7

Step 3

Tens	Ones

Tens	Ones
3	13
4	3
− 1	6
2	7

So, $43 - 16 = \underline{27}$.

Subtract. Regroup if you need to.
Use cubes and a workmat.

1.

Tens	Ones
3	7
− 1	5

Tens	Ones
5	0
− 1	3

Tens	Ones
7	6
− 2	8

Tens	Ones
4	5
− 2	7

Models to Subtract Two-Digit Numbers

Subtract. Regroup if you need to.
Use cubes and a workmat to help.

1.

Tens	Ones
7	16
8	6
− 2	8
5	8

2.

Tens	Ones
6	8
− 2	3

3.

Tens	Ones
5	4
− 1	5

4.

Tens	Ones
7	0
− 1	6

5.

Tens	Ones
4	3
− 2	7

6.

Tens	Ones
5	7
− 1	9

7.

Tens	Ones
6	7
− 3	4

8.

Tens	Ones
3	6
− 1	7

9. Reasoning Solve. Show your work.

Jamal has 54¢.

He wants to buy a toy that costs 70¢.

How much more money does he need?

(A) 14¢

(B) 16¢

(C) 24¢

(D) 26¢

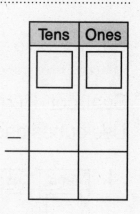

Tens	Ones
−	

Subtracting Two-Digit Numbers

Remember the steps for subtracting.

Step 1	**Step 2**	**Step 3**
Think: Are there enough ones to subtract?	Regroup the ones if you need to. Subtract.	Subtract the tens.

Write the problems in the frames. Find the difference.

38 − 13

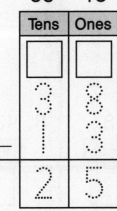

Tens	Ones
3	8
1	3
2	5

Regroup?   Yes   No

54 − 17

Tens	Ones
4	14
5	4
1	7
3	7

Regroup?   Yes   No

Write the problems in the frames. Find the difference.

1. 37 − 14

Tens	Ones

64 − 18

Tens	Ones

45 − 26

Tens	Ones

73 − 25

Tens	Ones

---

2. **Number Sense** Write a number to make this a subtraction with regrouping problem.

Tens	Ones
2	3

Subtracting Two-Digit Numbers

Write the subtraction problem. Find the difference.

1. $64 - 39$

Tens	Ones
5	14
$\not{6}$	$\not{4}$
$-$ 3	9
2	5

2. $65 - 16$

Tens	Ones
☐	☐
$-$	

3. $72 - 31$

Tens	Ones
☐	☐
$-$	

4. $56 - 29$

Tens	Ones
☐	☐
$-$	

5. $84 - 25$

Tens	Ones
☐	☐
$-$	

6. $34 - 16$

Tens	Ones
☐	☐
$-$	

7. $96 - 48$

Tens	Ones
☐	☐
$-$	

8. $43 - 27$

Tens	Ones
☐	☐
$-$	

9. Norma has 48 buttons. Connie has 29 buttons. How many more buttons does Norma have than Connie?

Ⓐ 29 buttons

Ⓑ 21 buttons

Ⓒ 19 buttons

Ⓓ 11 buttons

10. Number Sense Use each number only once. Write and solve the subtraction problem with the greatest difference.

1   2   4   5

Tens	Ones
☐	☐
$-$ ☐	☐

Name _____

Using Addition to Check Subtraction

When you subtract,
you start with the whole.
Then you take part away.
The other part is left.

$$
\begin{array}{r}
3\ 7 \quad \boxed{\text{Whole}} \\
-\ 1\ 2 \quad \boxed{\text{Part}} \\
\hline
2\ 5 \quad \boxed{\text{Part}} \\
\end{array}
$$

Tens	Ones

To check your work,
add to put the parts
back together.
Your answer should
be the whole.

$$
\begin{array}{r}
2\ 5 \quad \boxed{\text{Part}} \\
+\ 1\ 2 \quad \boxed{\text{Part}} \\
\hline
3\ 7 \quad \boxed{\text{Whole}} \\
\end{array}
$$

Tens	Ones

and   and

Subtract. Check your answer by adding.

1.

Tens	Ones
3	3
− 2	1

2.

Tens	Ones
8	6
−	9

3.

Tens	Ones
5	4
− 1	9

4.

Tens	Ones
6	3
− 3	7

Using Addition to Check Subtraction

Subtract. Check your answer by adding.
Write the missing part.

1.

$$\begin{array}{r} 5\;\;12 \\ \cancel{6}\;\cancel{2} \\ -1\;8 \\ \hline 44 \end{array}$$

$$\begin{array}{r} 1 \\ 44 \\ +1\;8 \\ \hline 62 \end{array}$$

2.

$$\begin{array}{r} 8\;3 \\ -2\;9 \\ \hline \end{array}$$

3.

$$\begin{array}{r} 7\;3 \\ -3\;7 \\ \hline \end{array}$$

4.

$$\begin{array}{r} 4\;8 \\ -2\;1 \\ \hline \end{array}$$

5.

$$\begin{array}{r} 9\;4 \\ -2\;8 \\ \hline \end{array}$$

6.

$$\begin{array}{r} 7\;5 \\ -1\;7 \\ \hline \end{array}$$

7. Lana has 39 moon stickers and 52 star stickers. How many more star stickers than moon stickers does she have?

(A) 13 more

(B) 17 more

(C) 23 more

(D) 27 more

8. Algebra Write the number that makes each number sentence true.

$60 - 20 = 20 + \underline{}$

$50 - 40 = 10 + \underline{}$

$70 - 30 = 10 + \underline{}$

$80 - 40 = 30 + \underline{}$

Problem Solving:
Two-Question Problems

Use the answer from the first question to answer the second question.

Tomas has 17 red toy cars and 8 blue toy cars.
How many toy cars does he have in all?

Follow Step 1 to answer this question.

Tomas gives 6 cars to his brother.
How many toy cars does Tomas have left?

Use the answer from the first question in Step 1 to answer this question. Follow Step 2.

Step 1

Add to find out how many toy cars Tomas has in all.

$$17 + 8 = 25$$

Step 2

Subtract the number of cars Tomas gives his brother.

$$25 - 6 = 19$$

Tomas has 19 cars left.

Use the answer from the first question to answer the second question.

I. Marta picked 12 red flowers and 9 pink flowers. How many flowers did Marta pick in all?

She gives 5 flowers to her teacher. How many flowers does Marta have left?

Step 1

Add to find out how many flowers Marta picked in all.

$$\_\_\_\_ + \_\_\_\_ = \_\_\_\_$$

Step 2

Subtract to find out how many flowers Marta has left.

$$\_\_\_\_ - \_\_\_\_ = \_\_\_\_$$

Marta has _____ flowers left.

Two-Question Problems

Solve. Use the answer from the first question to answer
the second question.

1. Barb has 12 pink bows and
   13 green bows. How many
   bows does she have in all?   **25** bows

   Barb gives 9 bows to her sister.
   How many bows does she have left?   **16** bows

2. Amanda has 11 eggs in a carton.
   She has 16 eggs in a bowl.
   How many eggs does she have in all?   _____ eggs

   Amanda cooks 12 eggs for her
   family's breakfast. How many eggs
   does she have now?   _____ eggs

3. Marcos had 20 quarters.
   He spent 7 quarters.
   Then he spent 5 quarters.

   How many quarters does
   Marcos have now?

   Ⓐ 8 quarters

   Ⓑ 12 quarters

   Ⓒ 13 quarters

   Ⓓ 32 quarters

4. **Estimation** 21 people were
   at the lake. Then 42 more
   people joined them.

   At 5:00, 30 people left.
   About how many people
   are still at the lake?

   Ⓐ about 50 people

   Ⓑ about 30 people

   Ⓒ about 40 people

   Ⓓ about 20 people

Adding Money

Adding money is the same as adding two-digit numbers.

Add two-digit numbers

Tens	Ones
☐	
3	5
+ 2	8
6	3

Add money.

Tens	Ones
☐	
3	5¢
+ 2	8¢
6	30¢

Remember to write
the ¢ sign in your answer.

Add to find the total amount.

1.

Tens	Ones
☐	
1	8
+ 4	7
6	5

Tens	Ones
☐	
1	8¢
+ 4	7¢

2.

Tens	Ones
☐	
3	3
+ 2	5

Tens	Ones
☐	
3	3¢
+ 2	5¢

3. Estimation Sarah Spends 25¢ on an apple.
Sarah has 60¢. Does she have enough ¢ to
buy juice for 39¢ too? Circle **yes** or **no**.

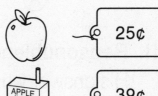

yes   no

Adding Money

Add to find the total amount.

1.
```
    2 | 4 ¢
  + 4 | 8 ¢
```
7 2¢

2.
```
    5 | 5 ¢
  + 3 | 6 ¢
```

3.
```
    2 | 9 ¢
  + 2 | 6 ¢
```

4.
```
    1 | 8 ¢
  + 6 | 4 ¢
```

5.
```
    2 | 4 ¢
  + 4 | 3 ¢
```

6.
```
    3 | 8 ¢
  + 4 | 7 ¢
```

7.
```
    5 | 9 ¢
  + 2 | 0 ¢
```

8.
```
    2 | 6 ¢
  + 6 | 7 ¢
```

9. Carlos buys a toy car for 38¢.

   Jessica buys a toy car for 46¢.

   How much money did they spend altogether?

   84¢   82¢   76¢   72¢
   (A)   (B)   (C)   (D)

10. Della buys a taco for 62¢.

    She buys taco sauce for 18¢.

    How much money did Della spend altogether?

    70¢   76¢   80¢   84¢
    (A)   (B)   (C)   (D)

11. **Reasonableness** Wade added 61¢ and 28¢.

    His answer was 89¢. Was he correct? Explain.

Estimating Sums

Use mental math to **estimate.**

22¢

and

16¢

Think: Add the tens first.

20¢ and 10¢ is ⠿30⠿ ¢.

Think: Add the ones next.

⠿2⠿ ¢ and ⠿6⠿ ¢ is ⠿8⠿ ¢ more.

You have 40¢.

Do you have enough money?

(yes)   no

Estimate. Circle **yes** or **no** to answer the question.

I.

24¢

and

15¢

_____ ¢ and _____ ¢ is _____ ¢.

_____ ¢ and _____ ¢ is _____ ¢ more.

You have 50¢.

Do you have enough money?

yes   no

2.

36¢

and

29¢

_____ ¢ and _____ ¢ is _____ ¢.

_____ ¢ and _____ ¢ is _____ ¢ more.

You have 60¢.

Do you have enough money?

yes   no

Estimating Sums

Estimate. Circle **yes** or **no** to answer the question.

 37¢ 12¢ 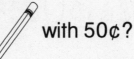49¢ 30¢ 24¢

1. Can you buy and with 50¢?   yes

   no

2. Can you buy and with 70¢?   yes

   no

3. Can you buy and with 50¢?   yes

   no

4. Can you buy and with 80¢?   yes

   no

5. Reanna wants to buy the ruler and the lock.
   About how much money does she need?

   (A) about 30¢   (C) about 50¢

   (B) about 40¢   (D) about 60¢

6. **Reasoning** Sam has 45¢. He has exactly enough
   money to buy the lock for 30¢ and an apple.
   How much does the apple cost?

   10¢   15¢   20¢   25¢
   (A)   (B)   (C)   (D)

Ways to Add

Use **mental math** to add.
43 + 20
Count up by tens. 43, 53, 63.

$43 + 20 = \underline{63}$

Use **cubes** to add.
27 + 18
Regroup 10 ones for one ten.

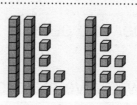

$27 + 18 = \underline{45}$

Use **paper and pencil** to add.
45 + 15

$$\begin{array}{r} \boxed{1} \\ 4\,5 \\ +\,1\,5 \\ \hline 0 \end{array}$$

Write 1 ten over the tens column.

$45 + 15 = \underline{60}$

Use a **calculator** to add.
56 + 29

$56 + 29 = \underline{85}$

Circle how you will solve the problem. Then add.

1. mental math
   cubes
   paper and pencil
   calculator

   $34 + 23 = \underline{57}$

2. mental math
   cubes
   paper and pencil
   calculator

   $46 + 30 = \underline{\quad}$

3. mental math
   cubes
   paper and pencil
   calculator

   $54 + 17 = \underline{\quad}$

4. mental math
   cubes
   paper and pencil
   calculator

   $73 + 18 = \underline{\quad}$

Ways to Add

Circle how you will solve the problem. Then add.

1. $\begin{array}{r} 5\ 6 \\ +\ 3\ 8 \\ \hline 9\ 4 \end{array}$ mental math

(paper and pencil)

2. $\begin{array}{r} 3\ 5 \\ +\ 2\ 4 \\ \hline \end{array}$ mental math

paper and pencil

Write the way you will solve the problem.
Then add and write the sum.

3. 61 + 13 = _____

_____

4. 28 + 38 = _____

_____

5. Damien has 48 red marbles. He has 39 blue marbles.
How many marbles does he have in all?

71   77   79   87
(A)   (B)   (C)   (D)

How did you solve the problem?

(A) mental math   (C) paper and pencil

(B) calculator   (D) cubes

6. **Number Sense** Write a problem that you
would solve with a calculator. Explain why.
Then use a calculator to find the answer.

_____ + _____ = _____

_____

Subtracting Money

Subtracting money is the same as subtracting
two-digit numbers.

$$
\begin{array}{r}
5\ 1¢ \\
-\ 2\ 2¢ \\
\hline
\end{array}
$$

Think of the pennies as ones
and the dimes as tens.

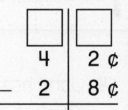

Tens	Ones
4	11
5	1¢
− 2	2¢
2	9¢

Remember to write the cents sign in your answer.

Subtract to find the difference.

1.

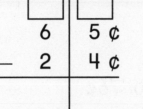

$$
\begin{array}{r}
5\ \ 9¢ \\
-\ 2\ \ 4¢ \\
\hline
3\ \ 5¢
\end{array}
$$

$$
\begin{array}{r}
6\ \ 5¢ \\
-\ 2\ \ 4¢ \\
\hline
\end{array}
$$

$$
\begin{array}{r}
7\ \ 3¢ \\
-\ 5\ \ 7¢ \\
\hline
\end{array}
$$

$$
\begin{array}{r}
4\ \ 2¢ \\
-\ 2\ \ 8¢ \\
\hline
\end{array}
$$

2.

$$
\begin{array}{r}
8\ \ 0¢ \\
-\ 2\ \ 9¢ \\
\hline
\end{array}
$$

$$
\begin{array}{r}
7\ \ 2¢ \\
-\ 3\ \ 6¢ \\
\hline
\end{array}
$$

$$
\begin{array}{r}
6\ \ 0¢ \\
-\ 4\ \ 8¢ \\
\hline
\end{array}
$$

$$
\begin{array}{r}
4\ \ 8¢ \\
-\ 1\ \ 8¢ \\
\hline
\end{array}
$$

3. Reasoning Greg has 58¢. He spends 25¢.
How much money does Greg have left?

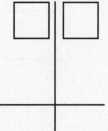

Greg has _____ left.

Subtracting Money

Subtract to find the difference.

1.
```
   ☐ ☐
   6  4 ¢
 - 3  8 ¢
 ─────────
```

2.
```
   ☐ ☐
   8  3 ¢
 - 3  9 ¢
 ─────────
```

3.
```
   ☐ ☐
   6  8 ¢
 - 4  7 ¢
 ─────────
```

4.
```
   ☐ ☐
   7  5 ¢
 - 3  7 ¢
 ─────────
```

5.
```
   ☐ ☐
   5  7 ¢
 - 1  9 ¢
 ─────────
```

6.
```
   ☐ ☐
   9  2 ¢
 - 7  1 ¢
 ─────────
```

7.
```
   ☐ ☐
   4  6 ¢
 - 1  2 ¢
 ─────────
```

8.
```
   ☐ ☐
   9  3 ¢
 - 4  4 ¢
 ─────────
```

9. Jane has 89¢ in her pocket.

   She buys a teddy bear pin for 76¢.

   How much money does Jane have left?

   13¢   14¢   15¢   16¢
   Ⓐ   Ⓑ   Ⓒ   Ⓓ

10. **Journal** Write a story for this problem: 55¢

    Then solve the problem.   − 49¢

    _____

    _____

    _____

    _____

Estimating Differences

Estimate to solve.

You have 46¢.
You buy:

Will you have more or
less than 20¢ left?

Subtract the tens first.

40¢ − ̲2̲0̲¢̲ is ̲2̲0̲¢̲

Think about the ones.

(more)

46¢ − 24¢ is   than 20¢.

less

Estimate to solve.
Circle **more** or **less** to complete each sentence.

1. You have 68¢.
   You buy:

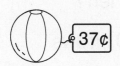

   Will you have more or
   less than 30¢ left?

   Subtract the tens first.

   60¢ − ____¢ is ____¢

   Think about the ones.

   more

   68¢ − 37¢ is   than 30¢.

   less

---

2. You have 70¢.
   You buy:

   Will you have more or
   less than 30¢ left?

   Subtract the tens first.

   70¢ − ____¢ is ____¢

   Think about the ones.

   more

   70¢ − 42¢ is   than 30¢.

   less

Estimating Differences

Estimate. Circle **is more than** or **is less than** to complete each sentence.

1.   71 − 33   is more than   40.
      (is less than)

2.   70 − 42   is more than   30.
                 is less than

3.   56 − 24   is more than   30.
                 is less than

4.   85 − 17   is more than   70.
                 is less than

5.   64 − 23   is more than   40.
                 is less than

6.   48 − 26   is more than   20.
                 is less than

7. A stand had 93 straws. It sold 45 cans of juice.
   Each can had one straw. How many straws were left?

   (A) less than 20 straws   (C) less than 40 straws

   (B) less than 30 straws   (D) less than 50 straws

8. **Estimation** There were 40 people at the movie.
   18 people left. About how many people are
   still at the movie?

   (A) about 10 people   (C) about 30 people

   (B) about 20 people   (D) about 40 people

© Pearson Education, Inc. 2

Ways to Subtract

Use **mental math** to subtract 75 − 20.
Count back 2 tens. 75, 65, 55.

$75 - 20 = \underline{55}$

Use **cubes** to subtract 38 − 12.

Show 38. Take away 1 ten.
Then take away 2 ones.

Tens	Ones

$38 - 12 = \underline{26}$

Use **paper and pencil** to subtract 60 − 23.

Regroup 1 ten as 10 ones.

5	10

$$\begin{array}{r} \cancel{6}\cancel{0} \\ -\;2\;\;3 \end{array}$$

$60 - 23 = \underline{37}$

Use a **calculator** to subtract 85 − 59.

$85 - 59 = \underline{26}$

Circle how you will solve the problem.
Then subtract.

1. mental math
   cubes
   paper and pencil
   calculator

   75 − 10 = ____

2. mental math
   cubes
   paper and pencil
   calculator

   49 − 22 = ____

Ways to Subtract

Circle the way you will solve the problem. Then subtract.

1.
$$\begin{array}{r} \cancel{5}\;\cancel{17} \\ 6 \;\; 7 \\ -\; 3 \;\; 8 \\ \hline 2 \;\; 9 \end{array}$$

mental math

(paper and pencil)

2.
$$\begin{array}{r} 8\;5 \\ -\;5\;4 \\ \hline \end{array}$$

mental math

paper and pencil

Write the way you will solve the problem.
Then subtract and write the difference.

3. 70 − 46 = _____

_____

4. 92 − 27 = _____

_____

5. Melissa decorates a book cover with stickers.
   She uses 52 star stickers and 38 moon stickers.
   How many more star stickers than moon stickers did she use?

12	14	24	26
(A)	(B)	(C)	(D)

6. **Algebra** Fong has 8 dimes.
   He wants to buy a card for 50¢.
   Which problem shows how much money he will have left?

$$\begin{array}{r} 8¢ \\ -\;5¢ \\ \hline 3¢ \end{array} \qquad \begin{array}{r} 50¢ \\ -\;8¢ \\ \hline 42¢ \end{array} \qquad \begin{array}{r} 80¢ \\ -\;5¢ \\ \hline 75¢ \end{array} \qquad \begin{array}{r} 80¢ \\ -\;50¢ \\ \hline 30¢ \end{array}$$

    (A)   (B)   (C)   (D)

Problem Solving: Try, Check, and Revise

Use the chart to solve the problem.

Animal Stickers	
Animal	**Price**
Elephant	33¢
Lion	18¢
Tiger	25¢
Zebra	21¢

Ken collects animal stickers.
He paid 43¢ for two stickers.
Which stickers did he buy?

Find two stickers that add up to 43¢.

Try: Pick two numbers.   25¢ and 21¢
              Add the numbers.   25¢ + 21¢ = _46¢_

Check: Is the sum 43¢? No.

Revise: Pick two other numbers.   18¢ and 25¢
              Add the numbers.   18¢ + 25¢ = _43¢_
              Is the sum 43¢? Yes.

Ken bought the lion and tiger stickers.

Use the chart to solve the problem.
Try, check, and revise (if necessary.)

I. Nina paid 51¢ for two stickers. Which stickers did she buy?

Try: 33¢ and _21¢_

Check: 33¢ + _21¢_ = _54¢_

         Is the sum 51¢? _No_.

Revise: 33¢ + _____ = _____

Nina bought the _____ and _____ stickers.

Problem Solving: Try, Check, and Revise

Use the chart to solve.
Try, check, and revise
(if you need to)
to solve each problem.

Dog Treat Prices	
Dog Treat	**Price**
Biscuit	36¢
Bone	34¢
Twist	29¢
Stick	23¢

1. Marty paid 65¢ for two dog treats.
   Which two treats did she buy?

   Ⓐ biscuit and bone   Ⓒ bone and stick

   Ⓑ twist and biscuit   Ⓓ stick and twist

2. Abdul paid 50¢ and got 27¢ in change.
   Which dog treat did he buy?

   biscuit   bone   twist   stick
   Ⓐ   Ⓑ   Ⓒ   Ⓓ

3. **Geometry** Jill paid 75¢ for a ring.
   She got 7¢ in change.
   Which type of stone does her ring have?

   Ⓐ ☐

   Ⓑ ◯

   Ⓒ △

   Ⓓ ▭

Ring Prices	
Stone Shape	**Price**
Square	62¢
Circle	54¢
Triangle	68¢
Rectangle	79¢

Flat Surfaces, Vertices, and Edges

Some solid figures have **flat surfaces** or **Faces**. Some have **edges** and **vertices**.

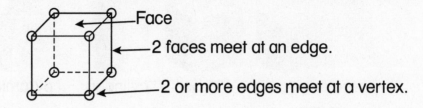

Face
2 faces meet at an edge.
2 or more edges meet at a vertex.

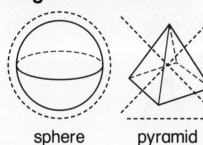 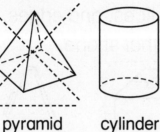  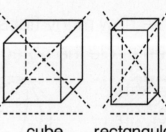

sphere   pyramid   cylinder   cone   cube   rectangular prism

Put an X on the solid figures that have edges.
Underline the solid figures that have vertices.
Circle the solid figure that does not have a flat surface.

Write the number of flat surfaces or faces, edges, and vertices. Use solid figures to help you.

1.

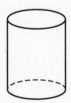

flat surfaces ___2___

edges _____

vertices _____

2.

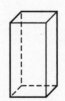

faces _____

edges _____

vertices _____

Flat Surfaces, Vertices, and Edges

 rectangular prism cube  cylinder  pyramid sphere cone

1. Write how many flat surfaces, vertices, and edges.
   Then circle the objects that have that shape.

A rectangular prism has ⬚ faces, ____ vertices, and ____ edges.

2. Ming's shape has 2 flat surfaces. It has no edges and no vertices. What shape is it?

   Ⓐ
   Ⓑ
   Ⓒ
   Ⓓ

3. Kim's shape has no flat surfaces. It has no edges and no vertices. What shape is it?

   Ⓐ
   Ⓑ
   Ⓒ
   Ⓓ

4. **Algebra** How many edges do these two shapes have in all? Write a number sentence.

 +

____ + ____ = ____

The two shapes have ____ edges in all.

Relating Plane Shapes to Solid Figures

If you trace the flat surfaces, or faces of solid figures,
you will get these plane shapes.

square

square   rectangle   circle   triangle

Use solid figures in your classroom.

Trace one flat surface or face.

Write the name of the shape you traced.

1. 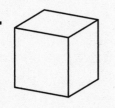 _____

2.  _____

3. 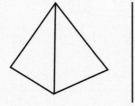 _____

4. 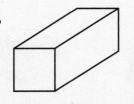 _____

Relating Plane Shapes to Solid Figures

Circle the solid figure or figures that have flat surfaces
or faces you can trace to make the plane shape.

I.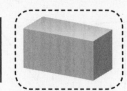

2.

3. Dionne traces a square
using a solid shape.
Which solid shape does
he have?

Ⓐ

Ⓑ

Ⓒ

Ⓓ

4. Which object did Maggie
use to trace the rectangle?

Ⓐ

Ⓑ

Ⓒ GUM

Ⓓ

5. **Geometry** Circle the block or blocks Vincent
can trace to draw the bug.

Making New Shapes

You can make larger shapes from smaller shapes.

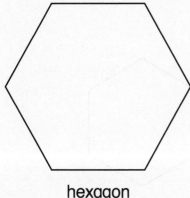

hexagon

parallelogram

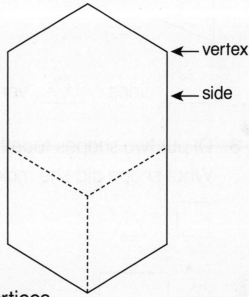

← vertex

← side

Use pattern blocks.

Put 2 parallelograms and a hexagon together to make this shape.

This shape has __6__ sides and __6__ vertices.

Spatial Thinking Use the pattern blocks shown to make a larger shape.
Trace the smaller shapes on the larger shape.
Write the number of sides and vertices.

I.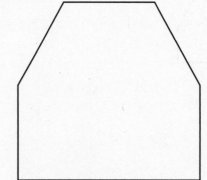

____ sides

____ vertices

Making New Shapes

Use pattern blocks to make the shape.
Trace and color to show one way to make it.
Write the number of sides and vertices.

1.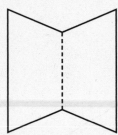

 sides   vertices

2.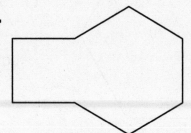

_____ sides   _____ vertices

3. Di put two shapes together.
What shape did she make?

Ⓐ

Ⓑ

Ⓒ

Ⓓ

4. Spatial Thinking Make
the triangle with 5 pattern
blocks.

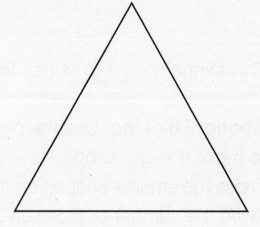

Cutting Shapes Apart

You can draw lines to cut a large shape
into smaller shapes.

Draw 1 line to make

2 triangles.

Draw 2 lines to make

4 squares.

Draw lines to make the shapes shown.

1. Draw 2 lines to cut
the square into

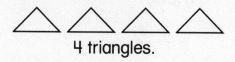

4 triangles.

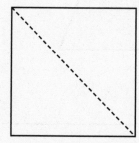

2. Draw 1 line to cut
the hexagon into

2 trapezoids.

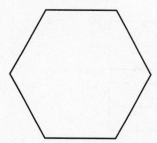

3. Journal Draw lines to cut the squares into rectangles.

Cutting Shapes Apart

Draw the number of lines shown to make new shapes.
Write the names of the shapes you made.

1. 2 lines

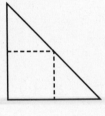

<u>square</u>

<u>triangle</u>

2. 1 line

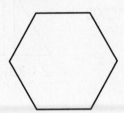

_____

_____

3. Dionne cut this shape into 2 triangles. Which drawing shows how he cut it?

4. Journal Draw a line from point A to point B. Write the names of the shapes you made.

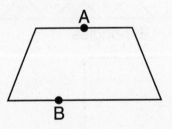

_____

_____

Practice 11-4

Congruence

These rectangles are not the same shape.

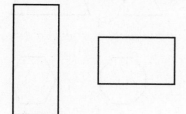

They are not congruent.

These rectangles are not the same size.

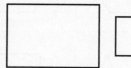

They are not congruent.

These rectangles are the same shape and same size.

They are congruent.

Are the shapes congruent? Circle **Yes** or **No**.

		Same Shape	Same Size	Congruent
I.	△ △	(Yes)	(Yes)	(Yes)
		No	No	No
2.	◻ ◻	Yes	Yes	Yes
		No	No	No
3.	⬡ ⬡	Yes	Yes	Yes
		No	No	No
4.	⬡ ⬡	Yes	Yes	Yes
		No	No	No

Congruence

Circle the shape that is congruent to the first shape.

1. |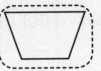

2. |

3.  |

4. Draw a shape that is congruent to this shape.

5. Draw two shapes that are congruent.

6. **Reasoning** Keisha put this plate on the table. Which plate below has a congruent shape?

    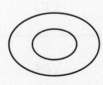

            Ⓒ   Ⓓ

Ways to Move Shapes

Move a shape block three different ways.

You can slide a shape to show a **translation**.	You can flip a shape to show a **reflection**.	You can turn a shape to show a **rotation**.
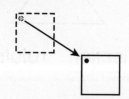	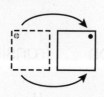	

---

1. Circle the shape that shows a **translation**.

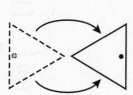 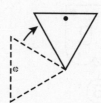 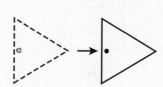

2. Circle the shape that shows a **reflection**.

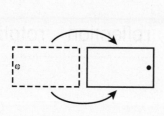 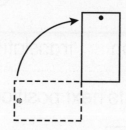 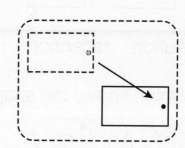

3. Circle the shape that shows a **rotation**.

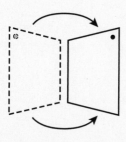 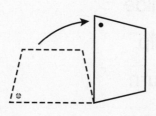 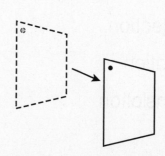

Ways to Move Shapes

Is it a translation, reflection, or rotation?
Circle the answer.

1.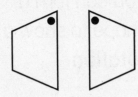

translation (reflection) rotation

2.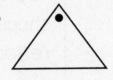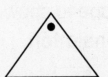

translation   reflection   rotation

3.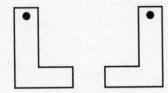

translation   reflection   rotation

4.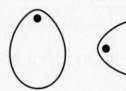

translation   reflection   rotation

5. Which shows the shape in its next position?

Ⓐ   Ⓑ   Ⓒ   Ⓓ

6. Geometry Draw lines to match each word on the left
with the correct word on the right.

reflection   slide

rotation   flip

translation   turn

Symmetry

Both parts match. This shape
has a line of symmetry.

 A line of
symmetry makes
2 matching parts.

The parts do not match.
This shape does not have
a line of symmetry.

Does the shape have a line of symmetry? Circle **Yes** or **No**.

1.

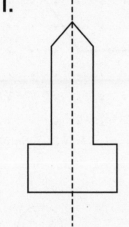

(Yes)   No

2.

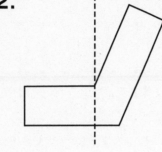

Yes   No

3.

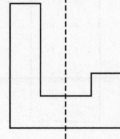

Yes   No

Draw the line of symmetry for each shape.

4.

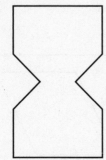

5.

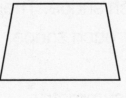

6.

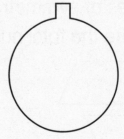

Symmetry

Does the shape have a line of symmetry?
Circle **yes** or **no**. If yes, draw a line of symmetry.

1.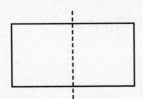
(yes)

no

2.
yes

no

Draw the matching part to make a shape with symmetry.

3.

4.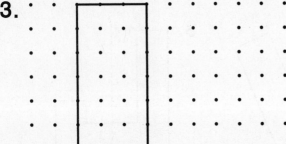

5. Which shape does not have a line of symmetry?

Ⓐ Ⓑ Ⓒ Ⓓ

6. Spatial Thinking Draw all of the possible lines of symmetry for each shape. Then write the total number for each shape.

 _____ line of symmetry

 _____ lines of symmetry

 _____ lines of symmetry

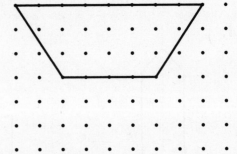

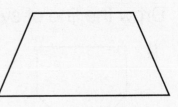

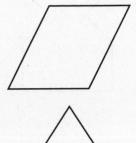

Problem Solving: Use Reasoning

Read the clues.

I am not a square.
I do not have 4 sides.
Which shape am I?

To find the shape, think:
It is not a square, so cross out the square.

It does not have 4 sides, so cross out
the shape with 4 sides.

Circle the shape that fits the clues.

Cross out the solid figures or shapes that do not fit
the clues. Circle the shape or solid figure that
answers the question.

1. I do not have edges.
   I am not a pyramid.
   Which shape am I?

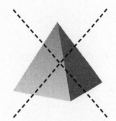 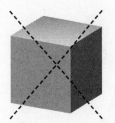 

2. I do not have 6 sides.
   I am not a circle.
   Which shape am I?

Problem Solving: Use Reasoning

Cross out shapes that do not match the clues.
Circle the shape that answers the question.

1. Which shape am I?
   I have 3 sides and 3 vertices.
   The lengths of my sides are equal.

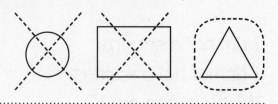

2. Which shape am I?
   I have more than 5 sides.
   The lengths of my sides are equal.

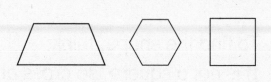

3. Which shape am I?
   I have 5 flat surfaces. You can
   trace my flat surfaces to make
   a triangle and a rectangle.

4. I have no vertices or edges.
   I have 2 flat surfaces.
   Which shows my shape?

Ⓐ

Ⓑ

Ⓒ

Ⓓ

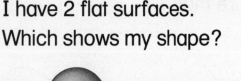

5. **Reasonableness** I have
   4 sides. The lengths of my
   sides are not equal. Which
   shows my shape?

Ⓐ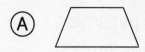

Ⓑ

Ⓒ

Ⓓ

Practice 11-8

Wholes and Equal Parts

Equal parts are the same shape and size.

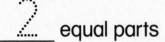 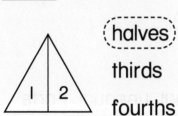

____ equal parts

(halves)
thirds
fourths

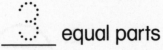 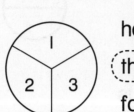

____ equal parts

halves
(thirds)
fourths

____ equal parts

halves
thirds
(fourths)

How many equal parts? Write the number of parts.
Circle halves, thirds, or fourths.

I. ____ equal parts

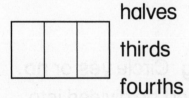

halves
thirds
fourths

2. ____ equal parts

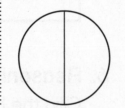

halves
thirds
fourths

3. ____ equal parts

halves
thirds
fourths

4. ____ equal parts

halves
thirds
fourths

5. ____ equal parts

halves
thirds
fourths

6. ____ equal parts

halves
thirds
fourths

7. **Spatial Thinking** Draw lines to show 2 equal parts.

  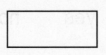

Wholes and Equal Parts

Write the number of parts.
Circle **equal** or **unequal**.

1.

   __2__ (equal) unequal parts

2.

   _____ equal unequal parts

Draw a line or lines to show equal parts.

3. fourths

4. thirds

5. Sami has a paper heart. Which shows how she could cut it into halves?

6. **Reasoning** Circle **yes** or **no**. Can the heart be divided into 3 equal parts?

   yes   no

Unit Fractions and Regions

A fraction can name one of the equal parts of a whole shape.

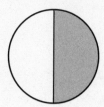 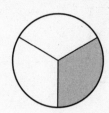 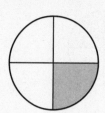

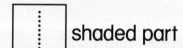 shaded part

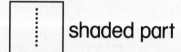 shaded part

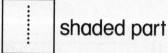 shaded part

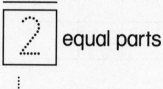 equal parts

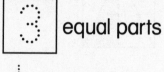 equal parts

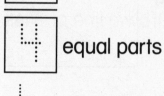 equal parts

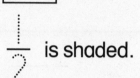 is shaded.

$\frac{1}{3}$ is shaded.

$\frac{1}{4}$ is shaded.

Color one part. Write how many shaded and equal parts.
Write the fraction.

I.

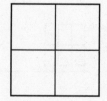

☐ shaded part

☐ equal parts

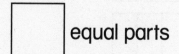 — is shaded.

2.

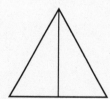

☐ shaded part

☐ equal parts

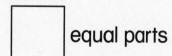 — is shaded.

Reteaching 12-2

Unit Fractions and Regions

Write the fraction for the shaded part of the shape.

1.

2.

_____

3.

_____

4.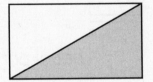

_____

5.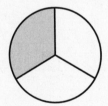

_____

6.

_____

7. Vinnie colored one part of the circle.
What fraction of the circle did he color?

Ⓐ $\frac{1}{2}$

Ⓑ $\frac{1}{3}$

Ⓒ $\frac{1}{4}$

Ⓓ $\frac{1}{6}$

8. Algebra Find the fraction for the shaded part of each shape. Look for a pattern. Which shape is missing?

 _____

Ⓐ

Ⓑ

Ⓒ

Ⓓ

Non-Unit Fractions and Regions

A fraction can name two or more equal parts of a whole shape.

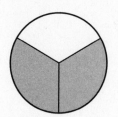

 shaded parts

 equal parts

$\dfrac{2}{3}$ is shaded.

Color the parts red.
Write the fraction for the shaded part.

I. Color 4 parts.

 parts are red.

☐ equal parts   _____ is red.

2. Color 2 parts.

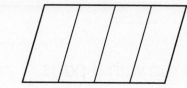

☐ parts are red.

☐ equal parts   _____ is red.

3. Color 5 parts.

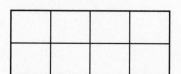

 parts are red.

☐ equal parts   _____ is red.

4. Color 3 parts.

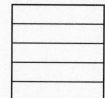

☐ parts are red.

☐ equal parts   _____ is red.

Reteaching 12-3

Non-Unit Fractions and Regions

Write the fraction for the shaded part of the shape.

1.

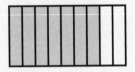

2.

_____

3.

_____

4.

_____

5.

_____

6.

_____

7. Jill has a rug with 8 parts. Four parts are white, and four parts are black. Which shows the rug?

   Ⓐ

   Ⓑ

   Ⓒ

   Ⓓ

8. **Geometry** Write the fraction for the shaded part of the rectangle.

   What shape does the shaded part make?

   _____

   The shaded part is

   a _____.

Estimating Fractional Parts of a Whole

Estimate how much of the pizza is left.

about 0   about $\frac{1}{2}$ (about 1)

It is close to a whole pizza, so it is about 1.

About how much is left?
Circle your answer.

1.

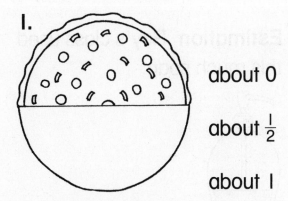

about 0

about $\frac{1}{2}$

about 1

2.

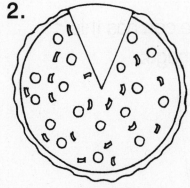

about 0

about $\frac{1}{2}$

about 1

3.

about 0

about $\frac{1}{2}$

about 1

4.

about 0

about $\frac{1}{2}$

about 1

Estimating Fractional Parts of a Whole

Circle the best estimate.
How much is shaded?

1.

about 0

about $\frac{1}{2}$

about 1

2.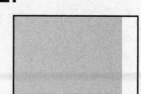

about 0

about $\frac{1}{2}$

about 1

3.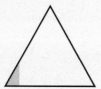

about 0

about $\frac{1}{2}$

about 1

4.

about 0

about $\frac{1}{2}$

about 1

5. A garbage can has this much garbage:

About how much of the garbage can is empty?

Ⓐ about 0

Ⓑ about $\frac{1}{4}$

Ⓒ about $\frac{1}{2}$

Ⓓ about 1

6. Estimation Ray's class used this much soap.

Which is the best estimate of how much soap is left?

Ⓐ about 1

Ⓑ about $\frac{1}{2}$

Ⓒ about $\frac{1}{4}$

Ⓓ about 0

Fractions of a Set

A fraction can name parts of a set or a group.

 shaded balls

___

balls in all

$\frac{2}{5}$ of the balls are shaded.

Color the parts.
Write the fraction for the part you color.

1. Color 2 parts blue.

2 blue stars

___

6 stars in all

$\frac{2}{6}$ of the stars are blue.

---

2. Color 3 parts green.

☐ green balloons

___

☐ balloons in all

___ of the balloons are green.

---

3. Color 5 parts red.

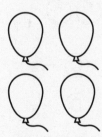

☐ red apples

___

☐ apples in all

___ of the apples are red.

Fractions of a Set

Color to show the fraction.

1.

$\frac{4}{5}$ of the apples are red.

2.

$\frac{3}{8}$ of the apples are red.

3.

$\frac{2}{4}$ of the apples are red.

4.

$\frac{2}{6}$ of the apples are red.

5. What fraction of the bananas are shaded?

Ⓐ $\frac{1}{2}$ Ⓒ $\frac{3}{4}$

Ⓑ $\frac{4}{7}$ Ⓓ $\frac{7}{4}$

6. What fraction of the cherries are shaded?

Ⓐ $\frac{12}{10}$ Ⓒ $\frac{2}{12}$

Ⓑ $\frac{10}{12}$ Ⓓ $\frac{1}{10}$

7. **Number Sense** Draw a picture to solve.

Sue has 9 baseball cards.
She gives 4 cards to Kris.
How many cards does Sue have left? _____

What fraction of the 9 cards does Sue have? _____

Problem Solving: Use Objects

There are 12 counters.

Find $\frac{1}{4}$ of a group of 12 counters.

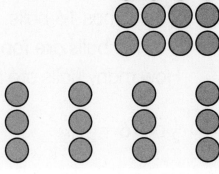

Sort the 12 counters into 4 groups.

1 of the 4 groups has 3 counters,

so $\frac{1}{4}$ of $\underline{12}$ = $\underline{3}$

Use counters. Sort the counters into groups to solve the problems.

1. Kiyo has 9 balloons. $\frac{1}{3}$ of the balloons are red. How many balloons are red?

   $\frac{1}{3}$ of _____ = _____

2. There are 10 apples in a bowl. $\frac{1}{2}$ of the apples are green. How many apples are green?

   $\frac{1}{2}$ of _____ = _____

3. Josh has 16 fish. $\frac{3}{4}$ of the fish have stripes. How many fish have stripes?

   $\frac{3}{4}$ of _____ = _____

4. There are 20 cars in a parking lot. $\frac{2}{5}$ of the cars are white. How many white cars are in the parking lot?

   $\frac{2}{5}$ of _____ = _____

Problem Solving: Use Objects

Solve the problems. Use counters to help.

1. Dennis has 16 balls.
   $\frac{1}{2}$ of the balls are footballs.
   How many balls are footballs?

   $\frac{1}{2}$ of 16 = _**8**_

2. A store has 25 bikes.
   $\frac{2}{5}$ of the bikes are red.
   How many bikes are red?

   $\frac{2}{5}$ of 25 = ____

3. A park has 18 swings.
   $\frac{3}{9}$ of them are tire swings.
   How many of the swings
   are tire swings?

   (A) 3 swings

   (B) 6 swings

   (C) 9 swings

   (D) 12 swings

4. Alice finds 12 shells.
   $\frac{1}{6}$ of the shells are
   black. How many shells
   are black?

   (A) 2 shells

   (B) 4 shells

   (C) 6 shells

   (D) 8 shells

5. **Reasonableness** Draw counters to help solve the problem.

There are 12 girls on a gymnastics team.
Less than $\frac{1}{4}$ of the girls are in second grade.
How many girls on the gymnastics team could
be in second grade?

_____ girls could be in second grade.

Name _____

Thinking About Attributes

Look at the object.

> **Length** is how long something is.
> **Weight** is how heavy an object is.
> **Capacity** is the amount a container can hold.

Can you measure the length of the milk container? __yes__

Can you weigh it? __yes__

Can you find out how much it holds? __yes__

Look at each object. Answer the questions yes or no.

1.

   Can you measure its length? _____

   Can you weigh it? _____

   Can you find out how much it holds? _____

2.

   2nd Grade **English**

   Can you measure its length? _____

   Can you weigh it? _____

   Can you find out how much it holds? _____

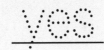

Thinking About Attributes

What tool would you use to measure the attribute?
Write or draw a tool.

scales   ruler   cubes   cups

I.   cup

capacity

2.

length

3.

weight

4.

length

5. What attribute is Hannah measuring?

   Ⓐ   weight

   Ⓑ   area

   Ⓒ   capacity

   Ⓓ   length

6. Journal Write **length**, **weight**, or **capacity**.

_____ the amount a container can hold

_____ the distance from one end of an object
to the other end

_____ how heavy an object is

Exploring Length

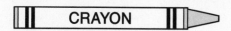

Look at the crayon.
About how many cubes long is the crayon?

Estimate.

When you **estimate** how long something is, you make a good guess.

I think the crayon is about _____ cubes long.

Then measure using cubes.

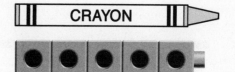

The crayon is about __5__ cubes long.

Estimate the length of each object.
Then measure using cubes.

I. I think the car is about _____ cubes long.

The car is about _____ cubes long.

2. I think the ribbon is about _____ cubes long.

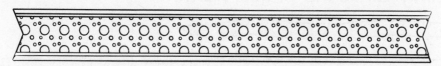

The ribbon is about _____ cubes long.

Exploring Length

Estimate the length of each line.
Then use paper clips to measure.

1.

Estimate: about ____4____ paper clips

Measure: about ____4____ paper clips

2. ▬▬▬▬▬▬▬▬▬▬

Estimate: about _____ paper clips

Measure: about _____ paper clips

Use paper clips to measure. About how long is each animal's picture?

3.

(A) 1 paper clip long

(B) 2 paper clips long

(C) 3 paper clips long

(D) 4 paper clips long

4.

(A) 4 paper clips long

(B) 3 paper clips long

(C) 2 paper clips long

(D) 1 paper clip long

5. **Spatial Thinking** Circle the longest worm.

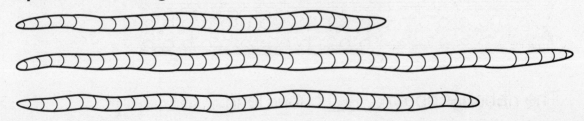

Measuring Length Using Non-Standard Units

How tall is the domino?
You can measure using different units.

Use cubes.   Use paper clips.

It is about   It is about

_4_ cubes tall.   _3_ paper clips tall.

If you use smaller units, you need to use more.

Measure using cubes. Then measure using paper clips.

1. Use cubes.   Use paper clips.

   It is about   It is about

   _____ cubes tall.   _____ paper clips tall.

2. Use cubes. It is about _____ cubes long.

Use paper clips. It is about _____ paper clips long.

Measuring Length Using Non-Standard Units

Use connecting cubes and paper clips to measure each object.

1.

about __3__ cubes long

about __2__ paper clips long

2.

about _____ cubes long

about _____ paper clip long

3. How tall is the nickel?

Ⓐ about 3 cubes

Ⓑ about 1 cube

Ⓒ about 2 paper clips

Ⓓ about 3 paper clips

4. **Estimation** The paintbrush is about 5 paper clips long. How long is it in cubes? Estimate first. Then measure.

Estimate:

about _____ cubes long

Measure:

about _____ cubes long

Inches, Feet, and Yards

This rope is about 1 inch long.

about 1 inch

This ribbon is about 1 foot long.
There are 12 inches in 1 foot.

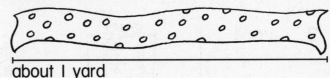
about 1 foot

This scarf is about 1 yard long.
There are 3 feet in 1 yard.

about 1 yard

About how long is each object? Circle the answer.

1.

    about 1 inch

    about 1 foot

    about 1 yard

2.

    about 1 inch

    about 1 foot

    about 1 yard

3.

    about 1 inch

    about 1 foot

    about 1 yard

4.

    about 1 inch

    about 1 foot

    about 1 yard

---

5. **Estimation** About how long is the
piece of paper?

about 1 inch   about 2 inches   about 6 inches

Inches, Feet, and Yards

Circle the object that is about each length.

1. a foot

2. a yard

3. an inch

4. Measure from your fingertips to your elbow.

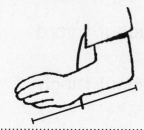

Estimate	Measure	Standard Units
about ____ paper clips	about ____ paper clips	about ____ inches

5. Sandy measures the length of a hockey stick. She says it is 4 units long. What unit did she use?

Ⓐ cubes

Ⓑ inches

Ⓒ feet

Ⓓ yards

6. Reasonableness
What is the height of the water bottle?

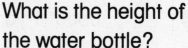
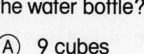

Ⓐ 9 cubes

Ⓑ 9 inches

Ⓒ 9 feet

Ⓓ 9 yards

Centimeters and Meters

This bead is about 1 centimeter long.

about 1 centimeter

There are 100 centimeters in 1 meter.
You would need 100 of these beeds to make 1 meter!

 ...

About how long is each object?
Circle the answer.

1.

about 1 centimeter

about 1 meter

2.

about 1 centimeter

about 1 meter

3.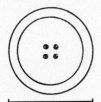

about 1 centimeter

about 1 meter

4.

about 3 centimeters

about 3 meters

Centimeters and Meters

Circle the object that is about each length.

1. I centimeter

2. I meter

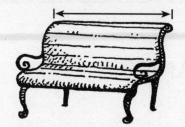

3. I centimeter

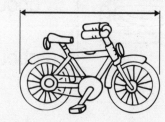

4. Which line is about I centimeter long?

(A) ▬▬▬▬▬▬▬▬▬▬▬▬▬▬

(B) ▬▬▬▬▬▬▬▬▬▬

(C) ▬

(D) ▬

5. Algebra How long are these 2 cubes joined together?
Write the missing numbers. Then add.

_____ + _____ = _____ centimeters

Exploring Perimeter

Find the perimeter of the shape.
Count the units on each side.
Add the units on all the sides.

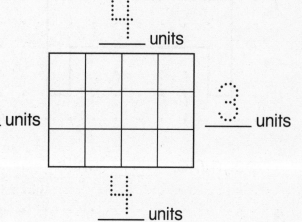

_4_ units

_3_ units

_3_ units

_4_ units

> **Perimeter** is the distance around the shape.

_4_ units + _3_ units + _4_ units + _3_ units = 14 units

The perimeter of the shape is _14_ units.

Find the perimeter of the shape.

I.

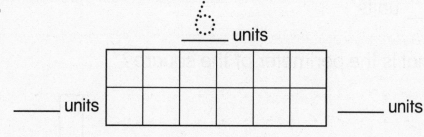

_6_ units

_____ units

_____ units

_____ units

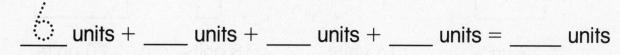

_6_ units + _____ units + _____ units + _____ units = _____ units

The perimeter is _____ units.

Reteaching 13-6

Exploring Perimeter

Find the perimeter of each shape.

1.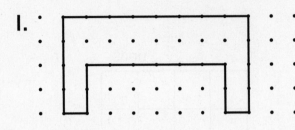

perimeter: _____ units

2.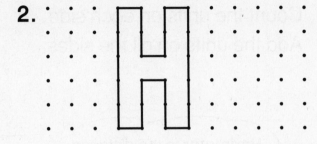

perimeter: _____ units

3.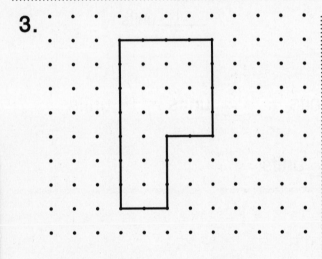

perimeter: _____ units

4. Find the perimeter of this shape.

Ⓐ 20 units

Ⓑ 21 units

Ⓒ 22 units

Ⓓ 23 units

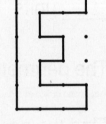

5. Geometry What is the perimeter of the square?

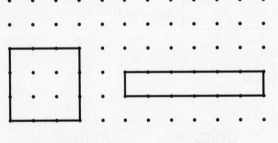

| 12 units | 16 units | 18 units | 20 units |
| Ⓐ | Ⓑ | Ⓒ | Ⓓ |

Practice 13-6

Name _____

Exploring Area

Look at this shape.

> Remember: **Area** is how many units it would take to cover the shape.

To find the area, count how many squares fit inside the shape.

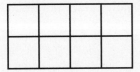

> To help you keep track, make an x in each square as you count it.

The area of the shape is __8__ square units.

Find the area of each shape.
Mark each square as you count.

1.

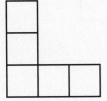

The area is ____
square units.

2.

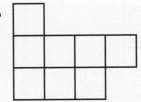

The area is ____
square units.

3.

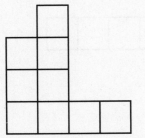

The area is ____
square units.

4.

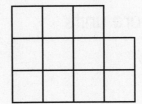

The area is ____
square units.

Exploring Area

Find the area of each shape.

1.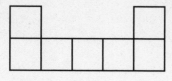

area: **7** square units

2.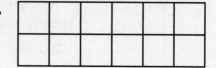

area: _____ square units

3.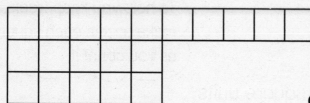

area: _____ square units

4. What is the area of the figure?

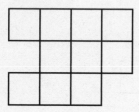

(A) 9 square units

(B) 10 square units

(C) 11 square units

(D) 12 square units

5. Geometry Which figure has an area of 6 square units?

(A)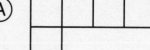

(B)

(C)

(D)

Practice 13-7

Problem Solving: Use Objects

Measure the space inside a shape. Use square tiles.

> **Area** is the space inside a shape.

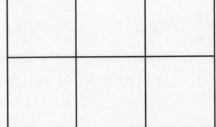

Place a tile on each box in the shape.
Count the tiles.

The area is __6__ square units.

> **Perimeter** is the distance around a shape.

Now, measure the distance around the shape.

Place tiles all around the shape.
Count the tiles.

The perimeter is __10__ square units.

Find the area and the perimeter of the shape.

I.

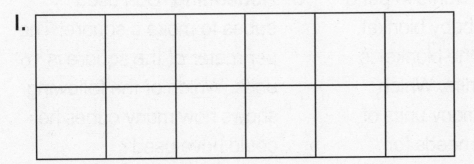

The area is _____ square units.

The perimeter is _____ square units.

Problem Solving: Use Objects

Use square tiles. Make a square. Find the perimeter.

1. The area is 9 square units.

   Perimeter = _12_ units

Use square tiles. Draw the rectangle on the grid. Find the area.

2. The perimeter is 10 units.

   Area = _____ square units

3. The perimeter is 16 units.

   Area = _____ square units

4. Mrs. Feltner wants to put a border on a baby blanket. The area of the blanket is 12 square units. Which shows how many units of material she needs for the border?

   (A) 12 units

   (B) 14 units

   (C) 15 units

   (D) 21 units

5. **Reasoning** Dan used cubes to make a square. The perimeter of the square is 16 units. Which of the following shows how many cubes he could have used?

   (A) 4 cubes

   (B) 8 cubes

   (C) 9 cubes

   (D) 16 cubes

Exploring Capacity

Capacity is the amount a container holds.
A large object holds more.
A small object holds less.

Which object holds more?	Which object holds less?

Circle the object that holds more.

I.

Circle the object that holds less.

2.

Circle the object that holds more.

3.

Name _____

Practice
14-1

Exploring Capacity

Which object holds the most?

1.

(A)

(B)

(C)

(D)

2.

(A)

(B)

(C)

(D)

Which object holds the least?

3.

(A)

(B)

(C)

(D)

4.

(A)

(B)

(C)

(D)

---

5. Spatial Thinking Draw a picture to solve.
Carlos drinks a mug of cocoa.
Draw an object that holds
more cocoa than his mug.

Practice 14-1

Measuring Capacity Using Non-Standard Units

Estimate how many cups of rice the container will hold.

Remember: When you estimate, you make a good guess.

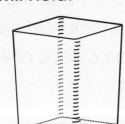

I think it will hold about ___4___ cups.

Think: Does the estimate make sense?

Use a cup and rice to measure and check.

The container holds about ___4___ cups.

Estimate how many cups of rice each container holds.
Then measure to check.

	Estimate.	Measure.
1.	about _____ cups	about _____ cups
2.	about _____ cups	about _____ cups
3.	about _____ cups	about _____ cups

Measuring Capacity Using Non-Standard Units

Use the picture to solve.

1. Brett has a cup of soup. How many cups of soup will the can hold?

Ⓐ 1 cup

Ⓑ 2 cups

Ⓒ 3 cups

Ⓓ 4 cups

2. Melanie looks at the fish. Can the tank hold more or less than 6 cups of water? Explain.

_____

_____

_____

_____

3. **Algebra** Write the missing number.

 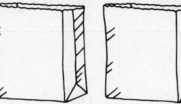 

4   cups of rice fill 1 sack

_____   cups of rice fill 3 sacks

Cups, Pints, and Quarts

You can use **cups**, **pints**, and **quarts** to
measure capacity.

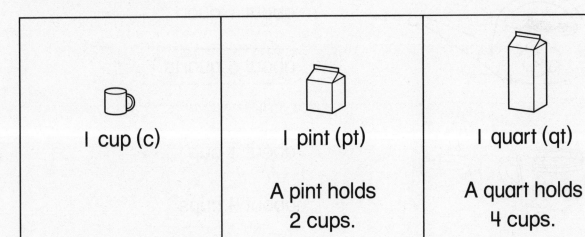

1 cup (c)	1 pint (pt) A pint holds 2 cups.	1 quart (qt) A quart holds 4 cups.

A cup holds ___less than___ a pint.

A quart holds ___more than___ a pint.

Circle the object that shows about the same capacity.

1. |

2. |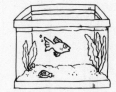

3. |

Cups, Pints, and Quarts

About how much does each object hold?
Circle the better estimate.

1.

about 1 quart

about 6 quarts

2.

about 1 cup

about 4 cups

3.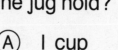

about 1 pint

about 10 pints

Solve each problem.

4. Does the thermos hold
   more or less than a cup?

_____

5. **Estimation** About
   how much does
   the jug hold?

   Ⓐ 1 cup

   Ⓑ 1 pint

   Ⓒ 1 quart

   Ⓓ 4 quarts

Liters

Liters are used to measure capacity.

I liter

This bottle of juice holds 1 liter.

This glass of juice holds

less _____ than 1 liter.

Circle the container that holds more than 1 liter.

I.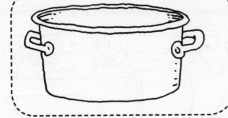

Circle the container that holds less than 1 liter.

2.

Juice

Circle the container that holds more than 1 liter.

3.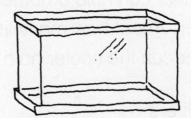

Liters

About how much does each object hold?
Circle the better estimate.

1.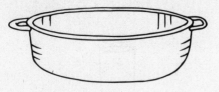

about 30 liters

(about 3 liters)

2.

about 10 liters

about 1 liter

3.

Ⓐ about 2 liters

Ⓑ about 20 liters

Ⓒ about 40 liters

Ⓓ about 80 liters

4.

Ⓐ about 1 liter

Ⓑ about 5 liters

Ⓒ about 10 liters

Ⓓ about 90 liters

5. Number Sense Solve.
The cooler can hold 6 bottles
of water. About how many liters
of water can the cooler hold?

_____ liters

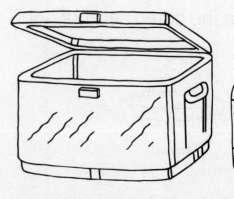

Exploring Weight

You can use a balance scale to measure **weight**.
The **heavier** object weighs
more and is lower on the scale.
The **lighter** object weighs
less and is higher on the scale.

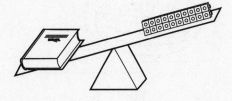

The book is ___heavier___. The cubes are ___lighter___.

Choose two objects. Hold one object in each hand to
compare weight. Draw the objects on a scale. Show
which object is heavier and which object is lighter.

I.

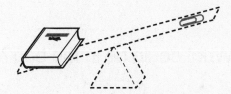

2.

3. **Reasoning** Draw how a scale would look if two
   objects weighed the same.

Name _____

Exploring Weight

Circle the object that weighs more.

1.

2.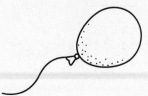

Circle the object that weighs less.

3.

4. What could be in the bag?

 Ⓐ

 Ⓑ

 Ⓒ

 Ⓓ

5. Reasoning Name three objects that weigh more than an apple.

_____

_____

_____

Ounces and Pounds

Ounces are used to measure light things.
Pounds are used to measure heavier things.

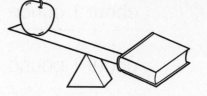

1 pound (lb) =
16 ounces (oz)

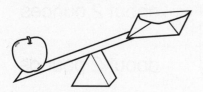

This letter weighs

about an ⟨ounce⟩.

This book weighs

about 1 ⟨pound⟩.

1. Circle the objects that weigh **less than** 1 ounce.

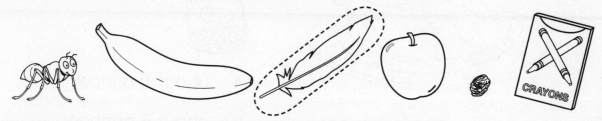

2. Circle the objects that weigh **more than** 1 pound.

3. **Journal** Draw two objects. Write if each weighs
more or less than a pound or an ounce.

Ounces and Pounds

About how much does each object weigh?
Circle the better estimate.

1.   (about 1 ounce)

   about 1 pound

2.   about 2 ounces

   about 2 pounds

3.   about 4 ounces

   about 4 pounds

4.  about 10 ounces

   about 10 pounds

5.

   about 9 ounces

   about 9 pounds

6.

   Ⓐ about 1 ounce

   Ⓑ about 5 ounces

   Ⓒ about 5 pounds

   Ⓓ about 50 pounds

7. **Journal** Draw something that weighs 1 ounce.
   Draw something that weighs 1 pound.
   Circle the object that weighs less.

one ounce   one pound

© Pearson Education, Inc. 2

Grams and Kilograms

Grams are used to measure light things.
Kilograms are used to measure heavier things.

1,000 grams (g) =
1 kilogram (kg)

This paper clip measures

about 1 ___gram___ .

This bag measures

about 1 ___kilogram___ .

1. Circle the objects that measure **more than** 1 gram.

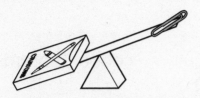

2. Circle the objects that measure **less than** 1 kilogram.

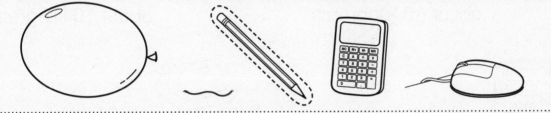

3. **Journal** Draw two objects. Write if each weighs
more or less than a kilogram.

Grams and Kilograms

About how much does each object measure?
Circle the better estimate.

1.

(about 1 gram)

about 1 kilogram

2.

about 3 grams

about 3 kilograms

3.

about 60 grams

about 60 kilograms

4.

about 10 grams

about 10 kilograms

5.

about 400 grams

about 400 kilograms

6.

about 30 grams

about 30 kilograms

7.

Ⓐ about 8 grams

Ⓑ about 8 kilograms

Ⓒ about 25 kilograms

Ⓓ about 80 kilograms

8. Reasonableness
Chad puts books
in his backpack.
Does the
backpack
measure about 4 grams or
about 4 kilograms?

_____

Problem Solving: Use Objects

You can use objects, or tools, to measure height, length, weight, and capacity. Use paper clips to measure length.

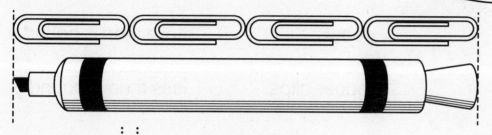

Height is how tall an object is.
Length is how long it is.
Weight is how heavy it is.
Capacity is how much it holds.

It is about __4__ paper clips long.

Use a scale and a book to measure weight. The book weighs about 1 pound.

The marker weighs _less than_ 1 pound.

Use objects to measure.

1. Use counting cubes to measure the height of a key.

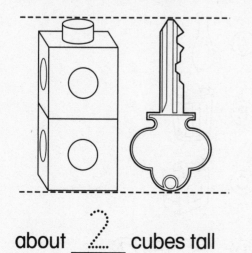

about __2__ cubes tall

2. Use cups of rice to measure the capacity of a jar.

about ____ cups

Problem Solving: Use Objects

Use paper clips to find the length. Use a balance scale
to find the weight. Circle **more than a pound** or
less than a pound.

		Length	Weight
1. 		about ____6____ paper clips	more than 1 pound (less than 1 pound)
2.		about _____ paper clips	more than 1 pound less than 1 pound

3. How many cups will this
paint bottle hold? Use
connecting cubes to find the
height of the paint bottle.

about _____ cups

about _____ cubes tall

4. Reasoning Nikki measured
an object in two ways.
It is 8 cubes tall.
It holds 1 cup of water.
Which shows what the object
could be?

Ⓐ

Ⓑ

Ⓒ

Ⓓ

Telling Time to Five Minutes

To tell time to five minutes, count by 5s for every number.

The time is

4:25.

There are 30 minutes in a half hour and 60 minutes in an hour.

The time is

4:30.

The hour hand moves from number to number in 60 minutes.

The time is

5:15.

Count by 5s.
Write the time.

1.

2.

3.

4.

Telling Time to Five Minutes

Write the time.

1.

2.

3.

4.

5. The time is 6:05. What number would the minute hand be pointing to on a clock?

6   5   2   I

(A)   (B)   (C)   (D)

6. Look at the clock. What time does it show?

(A) 12:45   (C) 12:55

(B) 12:50   (D) 1:00

7. Number Sense Look at the time on the first clock. What time will it be in five minutes? Show that time on the second clock.

Telling Time Before and After the Hour

There are different ways to say time before and after the hour.

6:15	6:30	6:45	2:35
15 minutes after 6 or **quarter past** 6	30 minutes after 6 or **half past** 6	45 minutes after 6 or **quarter to** 7	25 minutes **before** 3 or 35 minutes after 2

Count by 5s to tell the time. Write the time.

1. 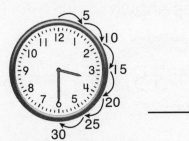 _____

30 minutes after _____

or **half past** _____

2.  _____

15 minutes after _____

or **quarter past** _____

3. **Reasoning** The time is 6:10. Is the hour hand closer to 6 or 7? Why?

_____

_____

Telling Time Before and After the Hour

Write the time or draw the hands to show the time.
Then write the time before or after the hour.

1.

quarter to ___11___

2.

half past _____

3. Joyce gets up at ten minutes before 7. Which clock shows this time?

Ⓐ

Ⓑ

Ⓒ

Ⓓ

4. Journal Write two ways to say the time shown.

_____

_____

_____

Estimating Time

About how long
does it take to
wash your face?

about 1 second   No, 1 second is too short.

(about 1 minute)   Yes, 1 minute is reasonable.
It makes sense.

about 1 hour   No, 1 hour is too long.

about 1 day   No, 1 day is too long.

Circle the amount of time each activity would take.

1. Drinking milk

about 1 minute

about 1 hour

about 1 day

2. Watching a TV show

about 1 second

about 1 hour

about 1 day

3. Going on a picnic

about 2 minutes

about 2 hours

about 2 days

4. Going on a trip

about 5 minutes

about 5 hours

about 5 days

Estimating Time

Choose the amount of time each activity would take.

1. making a
   sandwich

   (A) about 5 seconds

   (B) about 5 minutes

   (C) about 5 hours

   (D) about 5 days

2. visiting a
   friend

   (A) about 3 seconds

   (B) about 3 minutes

   (C) about 3 hours

   (D) about 3 days

3. going on
   vacation

   (A) about 10 seconds

   (B) about 10 minutes

   (C) about 10 hours

   (D) about 10 days

4. touching
   your nose

   (A) about 1 second

   (B) about 1 minute

   (C) about 1 hour

   (D) about 1 day

5. Bill mows the lawn.
   Megan rings the doorbell.
   Whose activity takes
   about 2 seconds?

   _____

6. **Estimation** You and a friend
   play "Pass the Potato."
   How many times do you think
   you can pass the potato in
   one minute?

   3 times   30 times

Using a Calendar

This calendar shows the month of March.
The list shows the months of the year in order.

January
February
March
April
May
June
July
August
September
October
November
December

Days of the week

Name of the month

March						
Sunday	Monday	Tuesday	Wednesday	Thursday	Friday	Saturday
	1	2	3	4	5	6
7	8	9	10	11	12	13
14	15	16	17	18	19	20
21	22	23	24	25	26	27
28	29	30	31			

Dates in
this month

There are __12__ months.

Look at the last date in the month to find how many days in March.

March is the __3rd__ month of the year.

There are __31__ days in March.

Use the calendar and list to answer the questions.

1. There are 52 weeks in a year. There are __5__ weeks in March.

2. What is the day after Wednesday? _____

3. What day is the 16th of March? _____

4. What is the date of the last Sunday in March? _____

5. What is the last month of the year? _____

Using a Calendar

Use the calendar to answer the questions.

| January | | | | | | |
S	M	T	W	T	F	S
						1
2	3	4	5	6	7	8
9	10	11	12	13	14	15
16	17	18	19	20	21	22
23	24	25	26	27	28	29
30	31					

| February | | | | | | |
S	M	T	W	T	F	S
		1	2	3	4	5
6	7	8	9	10	11	12
13	14	15	16	17	18	19
20	21	22	23	24	25	26
27	28					

| March | | | | | | |
S	M	T	W	T	F	S
		1	2	3	4	5
6	7	8	9	10	11	12
13	14	15	16	17	18	19
20	21	22	23	24	25	26
27	28	29	30	31		

| April | | | | | | |
S	M	T	W	T	F	S
					1	2
3	4	5	6	7	8	9
10	11	12	13	14	15	16
17	18	19	20	21	22	23
24	25	26	27	28	29	30

| May | | | | | | |
S	M	T	W	T	F	S
1	2	3	4	5	6	7
8	9	10	11	12	13	14
15	16	17	18	19	20	21
22	23	24	25	26	27	28
29	30	31				

| June | | | | | | |
S	M	T	W	T	F	S
			1	2	3	4
5	6	7	8	9	10	11
12	13	14	15	16	17	18
19	20	21	22	23	24	25
26	27	28	29	30		

| July | | | | | | |
S	M	T	W	T	F	S
					1	2
3	4	5	6	7	8	9
10	11	12	13	14	15	16
17	18	19	20	21	22	23
24	25	26	27	28	29	30
31						

| August | | | | | | |
S	M	T	W	T	F	S
	1	2	3	4	5	6
7	8	9	10	11	12	13
14	15	16	17	18	19	20
21	22	23	24	25	26	27
28	29	30	31			

| September | | | | | | |
S	M	T	W	T	F	S
				1	2	3
4	5	6	7	8	9	10
11	12	13	14	15	16	17
18	19	20	21	22	23	24
25	26	27	28	29	30	

| October | | | | | | |
S	M	T	W	T	F	S
						1
2	3	4	5	6	7	8
9	10	11	12	13	14	15
16	17	18	19	20	21	22
23	24	25	26	27	28	29
30	31					

| November | | | | | | |
S	M	T	W	T	F	S
		1	2	3	4	5
6	7	8	9	10	11	12
13	14	15	16	17	18	19
20	21	22	23	24	25	26
27	28	29	30			

| December | | | | | | |
S	M	T	W	T	F	S
				1	2	3
4	5	6	7	8	9	10
11	12	13	14	15	16	17
18	19	20	21	22	23	24
25	26	27	28	29	30	31

Spatial Thinking

1. What month comes just before May? _April_

2. What month comes just after August? _____

3. What day of the week is December 3? _____

4. Sara's birthday is in a month that has 5 Thursdays.
   Her birthday is on a Thursday, and is the 23rd of the month.
   What month is her birthday on this calendar?

   June   August   September   December
   Ⓐ   Ⓑ   Ⓒ   Ⓓ

Temperature: Fahrenheit and Celsius

You can measure temperature in **Fahrenheit** or **Celsius**.

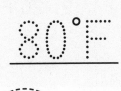 80°F 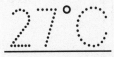 27°C

(hot)   cold

The higher the degree the warmer it is.

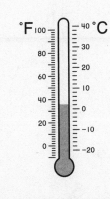

35°F   2°C

hot   (cold)

The lower the degree the colder it is.

Write the temperature in Fahrenheit and Celsius.
Circle hot or cold to tell about the temperature.

I.

_____   _____

hot   cold

2.

_____   _____

hot   cold

Reteaching **15-6**

Temperature: Fahrenheit and Celsius

Color to show the temperature.
Circle hot or cold to tell about the temperature.

I. 20°C   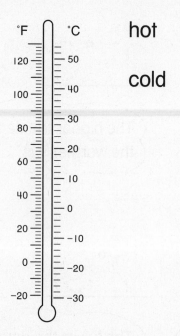   hot

   cold

2. 20°F      hot

   cold

What temperature does the thermometer show?

3.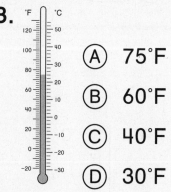

  (A) 75°F

  (B) 60°F

  (C) 40°F

  (D) 30°F

4.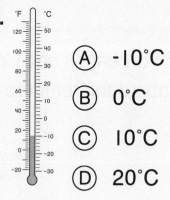

  (A) -10°C

  (B) 0°C

  (C) 10°C

  (D) 20°C

5.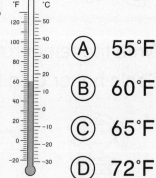

  (A) 55°F

  (B) 60°F

  (C) 65°F

  (D) 72°F

Reasoning Answer each question.

6. It is 32°C. Bianca goes outside to play. Should she wear sandals or boots?

_____

7. It is 32°F. Barry goes to the beach. Should he wear a swimsuit or a warm coat?

_____

Problem Solving:
Multiple-Step Problems

Read the problem. Follow the steps to solve.

Pat has 60 minutes before the bus comes.
It takes 20 minutes to dress for school.
It takes 20 minutes to eat breakfast.
How many extra minutes does Pat have?

Think: You need to figure out the number of extra minutes Pat has.

Step 1 Add the time Pat uses to dress and to eat:

$$20 + 20 = 40$$

Step 2 Subtract the time used from the time Pat has:

$$60 - 40 = 20$$

Pat has __20__ extra minutes.

Think: Does the answer make sense?

Use two steps to solve.

1. Andy has 30 minutes before the soccer game. It takes 15 minutes to dress. It takes 10 minutes to get to the park. How much extra time does Andy have before the game?

   Step 1

   $$15 + \rule{1cm}{0.4pt} = \rule{1cm}{0.4pt}$$

   Step 2

   $$\rule{1cm}{0.4pt} - \rule{1cm}{0.4pt} = \rule{1cm}{0.4pt}$$

   Andy has _____ extra minutes.

Problem Solving:
Multiple-Step Problems

Solve. Write a number sentence for each part of the problem.
Use base-ten blocks if you need to.

1. Kit spent 30 minutes on the slide. He spent
   20 minutes on the swings. How much time
   did he spend at the playground?
   Kit also spent 40 minutes in the
   picnic area. How much time did
   he spend at the park in all?

   $30 + 20 = 50$ minutes

   $50 + 40 = 90$ minutes

2. **Algebra** This week Tracey played baseball
   for 5 hours and soccer for 7 hours. How
   much time did she spend on both sports?
   Tracey spent 15 hours on sports.
   How much time did she spend at
   the swimming pool if the rest of
   her time was spent swimming?

   _____ hours

   _____ hours

3. Rita read a book for 50
   minutes. She watched TV for
   30 minutes. If Rita has 100
   minutes before bedtime,
   how much time does she
   have to take a bath?

   Ⓐ 35 minutes

   Ⓑ 30 minutes

   Ⓒ 25 minutes

   Ⓓ 20 minutes

4. Jerry watched a butterfly
   flap its wings for 15 seconds,
   fly for 7 seconds, and sit
   under a leaf for 27 seconds.
   For how long did Jerry watch
   the butterfly?

   Ⓐ 14 seconds

   Ⓑ 34 seconds

   Ⓒ 42 seconds

   Ⓓ 49 seconds

Organizing Data

Use this data to make a bar graph.

Children at Grand School sold
tickets to their school play.

Grade 1 sold 8 tickets.
Grade 2 sold 15 tickets.
Grade 3 sold 12 tickets.

Color the boxes to show the
number of tickets each grade sold.

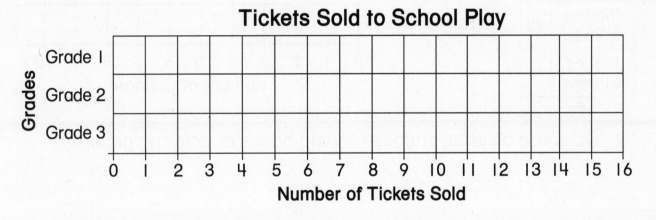

Tickets Sold to School Play

Use the bar graph to compare data.

1. How many tickets did Grade 3 sell? _12_

2. How many tickets did Grade 1 sell? _____

3. Which grade sold the fewest tickets? _____

4. Which grade sold the most tickets? _____

5. How many more tickets did Grade 3 sell than Grade 1? _____

6. Which grade sold more than 13 tickets? _____

Organizing Data

Use the table to make the bar graph.

Then use the bar graph to solve the problems.

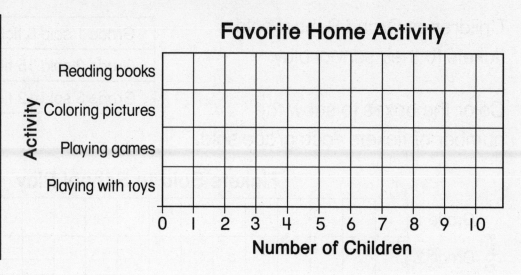

Home Activity	
Reading books	9
Coloring pictures	8
Playing games	10
Playing with toys	4

1. Did more children choose reading books or coloring pictures?

_____

2. Which activity is the favorite of the greatest number of children?

_____

3. Which activity is the favorite of the fewest number of children?

_____

4. Estimation About how many children were asked to vote for their favorite home activity?

(A) about 10 children   (C) about 30 children

(B) about 20 children   (D) about 40 children

Pictographs

A pictograph uses pictures or symbols to show information.
Write how many children chose each snack.

Each ☺ = 1 child

There are 9 symbols
for popcorn. So
9 children chose
popcorn.

Favorite Snacks

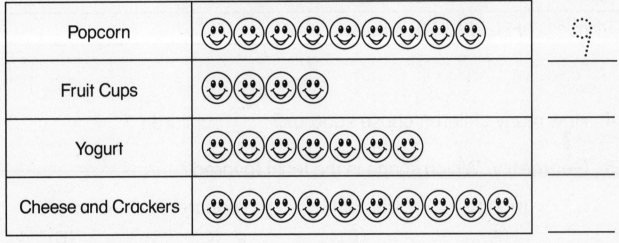

Popcorn	☺☺☺☺☺☺☺☺☺	9
Fruit Cups	☺☺☺☺	___
Yogurt	☺☺☺☺☺☺☺	___
Cheese and Crackers	☺☺☺☺☺☺☺☺☺☺	___

Use the graph to answer the questions.

1. How many children like
cheese and crackers best? _____ children

2. How many children like yogurt the best? _____ children

3. Which snack is the least favorite? _____

4. Which snack is favored by most children? _____

5. How many more children
like yogurt than fruit cups? _____ children

6. How many more children like
cheese and crackers than yogurt? _____ children

Pictographs

Use the tally chart to complete the pictograph.
Then use the pictograph to solve the problems.

Shapes	
Circle	TH‌L
Square	I I I I
Triangle	TH‌L I I I

Our Favorite Shapes	
1. Circle	
2. Square	
3. Triangle	

4. How many children chose squares? ___4___ children

5. **Geometry** Which shape is the least favored?

     triangle   rectangle   square   circle
      Ⓐ   Ⓑ   Ⓒ   Ⓓ

6. Look at the tally chart.
It shows favorite snacks.
Which graph matches
the tally chart?

Our Favorite Snacks	
Banana	I
Crackers	I I I
Yogurt	I I

Ⓐ
Our Favorite Snacks	
Banana	🍌
Crackers	◇ ◇ ◇ ◇
Yogurt	🥤 🥤 🥤

Ⓒ
Our Favorite Snacks	
Banana	🍌
Crackers	◇ ◇
Yogurt	🥤 🥤

Ⓑ
Our Favorite Snacks	
Banana	🍌 🍌
Crackers	◇ ◇ ◇
Yogurt	🥤 🥤

Ⓓ
Our Favorite Snacks	
Banana	🍌 🍌
Crackers	◇
Yogurt	🥤 🥤 🥤

Bar Graphs

The tally chart shows how children voted to name the class goldfish.

Use the data from the tally chart to make a bar graph.

Goldfish Names	
Flash	⊤⊣⊣⊢ I I
Goldie	⊤⊣⊣⊢
Rocky	⊤⊣⊣⊢ I I I
Bubbles	⊤⊣⊣⊢ ⊤⊣⊣⊢

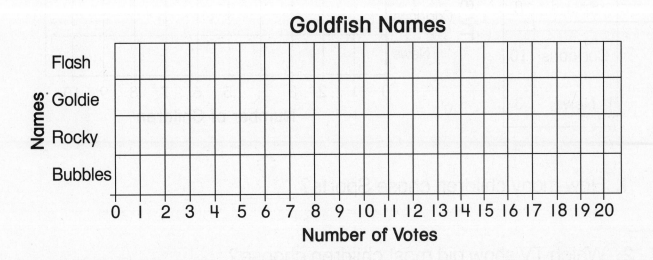

Goldfish Names

Names: Flash, Goldie, Rocky, Bubbles

Number of Votes: 0 1 2 3 4 5 6 7 8 9 10 11 12 13 14 15 16 17 18 19 20

Use the bar graph to answer the questions.

1. How many children voted for the name Goldie? _____

2. How many children voted for the name Flash? _____

3. Which name did most children choose? _____

4. Which name did the fewest children choose? _____

5. Did more children prefer the name Rocky or Flash? _____

6. **Journal** Ask classmates to vote for their favorite goldfish name. Make a tally chart to show how they voted. Then make a bar graph.

Bar Graphs

Use the tally chart to complete the bar graph.
Then use the bar graph to answer the questions.

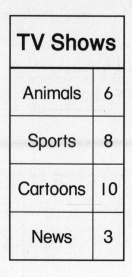

TV Shows	
Animals	6
Sports	8
Cartoons	10
News	3

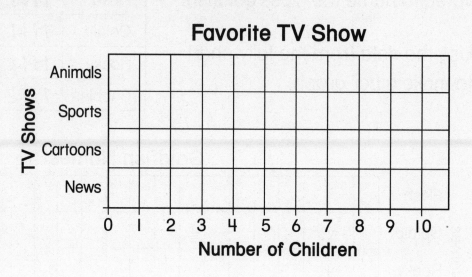

1. How many children chose Sports? __8__

2. Which TV show did most children choose? _____

3. Did more children choose News or Animals? _____

4. Which TV show did the fewest children choose?

Animals	Sports	Cartoons	News
Ⓐ	Ⓑ	Ⓒ	Ⓓ

5. Reasoning How would the bar graph change if two more children voted for Animals?

_____

_____

Coordinate Graphs

Coordinate graphs show where things are located.

The ordered pair (B, 1) names the location
of the fish on the graph.

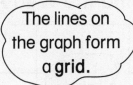

The lines on
the graph form
a **grid**.

Where is the mouse?
Start at 0 and go to A.
From A, go up.
Count the spaces.
The mouse is located at (A , 2).

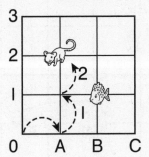

Where is the fly?
Start at 0 and go to B.
From B, go up.
Count the spaces.
The fly is located at (B , 2).

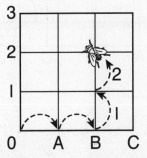

Write the ordered pair where each animal is located.

1.  (A , ___)

2. 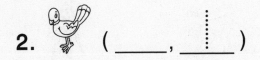 (___ , 1)

3. 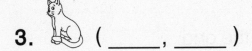 (___ , ___)

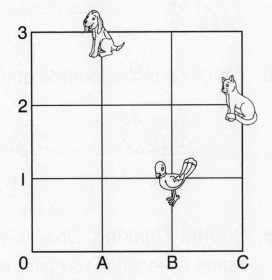

Coordinate Graphs

Write the ordered pair for the location of each animal.

Find the Wild Animals

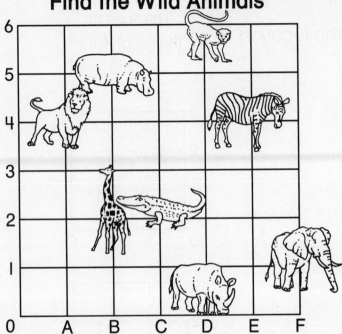

1. B, 5

2. _____

3.  _____

4. _____

5. Which animal is located at (C,2)?

Ⓐ   Ⓑ   Ⓒ   Ⓓ

6. Spatial Thinking Draw a wild bird on the grid.
Name its location using an ordered pair.

_____

Likely and Unlikely

You can predict if something is **more likely, less likely,**
or **equally likely** to happen.

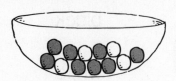

How many white marbles? **4**

How many shaded marbles? **8**

It is _**more**_ likely that you will pick a shaded marble.

It is _**less**_ likely that you will pick a white marble.

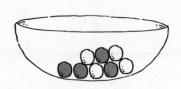

There are _**4**_ white marbles and

_**4**_ shaded marbles.

It is _**equally**_ likely that you will pick a white or shaded marble.

Answer the questions. Then write **more,**
less, or **equally** to complete the sentence.

1. How many apples? _____ apples

   How many pears? _____ pears

   It is _____ likely that you will pick a pear.

   It is _____ likely that you will pick an apple.

2. **Reasoning** If you have 4 shaded marbles and 4 white marbles
   why are you **equally likely** to pick a shaded or white marble?

   _____

Likely and Unlikely

If you were to spin once, which color
is the spinner **most likely** to land on?

1. 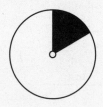 black

 (white)

2. 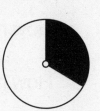 black

white

3. 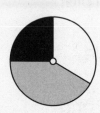 black

white

gray

4. 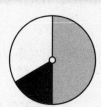 black

white

gray

If you were to spin once, which color
is the spinner **least likely** to land on?

5.

  Ⓐ black

  Ⓑ white

  Ⓒ gray

  Ⓓ brown

6.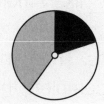

  Ⓐ black

  Ⓑ white

  Ⓒ gray

  Ⓓ brown

7. **Reasoning** If you were to draw one cube
out of the bag without looking, is it **more likely,
less likely,** or **equally likely** that you would
pick a white cube?

Certain, Probable, and Impossible

Words like **certain**, **probable**, and **impossible** tell about probability.

You pick one button from the jar.

It is ___certain___ that you will pick a black or a gray button.

Certain means it will happen.

There are more black buttons.

It is ___probable___ that you will pick a black button.

Probable means it is most likely to happen.

There are not any white buttons.

It is ___impossible___ that you will pick a white button.

Impossible means that it will <u>not</u> happen.

Look at the number of buttons in the jar.
Circle the button or buttons that tell about each probability.

You pick one button from the jar.

I. It is **certain** that you will pick

2. It is **probable** that you will pick

3. It is **impossible** that you will pick

Certain, Probable, and Impossible

Use the tally chart to help you answer the questions.
Circle the missing word to complete the sentence.

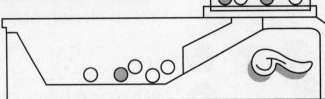

white	~~HHH~~ ~~HHH~~ //
gray	////

1. There are more _____ bouncy balls
   in the machine.

    white
   gray

2. You buy one bouncy ball. It is _____
   that you will buy a white bouncy ball.

   probable
   impossible

3. You buy another ball. It is _____ that you will
   buy a white bouncy ball or a gray bouncy ball.

   certain
   probable

4. Which best completes the sentence?

   If you buy one bouncy ball from the machine, it is _____
   that you will pick a black bouncy ball.

   less likely   probable   certain   impossible
       Ⓐ   Ⓑ   Ⓒ   Ⓓ

5. **Reasonableness** There are 28 red apples and
   7 green apples in a basket. Is it more probable to
   pick a red apple or a green apple? Why?

   _____

   _____

Problem Solving: Use a Graph

You can use the data on the graph to solve the problem.
How many more votes did the Tigers get than the Lions?

Votes for Team Name	
Wolves	🐺 🐺 🐺 🐺 🐺
Tigers	🐯 🐯 🐯 🐯 🐯 🐯 🐯 🐯 🐯 🐯 🐯
Lions	🦁 🦁 🦁 🦁 🦁 🦁 🦁 🦁 🦁

Count the Tigers and Lions on the graph.
Then subtract.

$$\underline{11} - \underline{9} = \underline{2}$$

There are __2__ more votes for Tigers than Lions.

Use the graph to solve the problem.
How many more children chose soccer than T-ball?

Game Choices

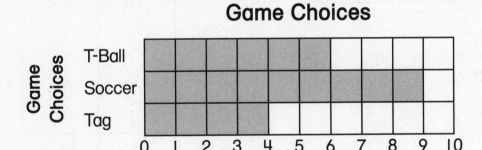

1. How many children chose soccer? __9__

2. How many children chose T-ball? ____

3. Subtract. ____ – ____ = ____ children

Problem Solving: Use a Graph

Use the bar graph to answer the questions.

Favorite Ice Cream

Kinds of Ice Cream											
Vanilla											
Chocolate											
Strawberry											

0   1   2   3   4   5   6   7   8   9   10
Number of Children

1. Which ice cream got the most votes?  chocolate

2. Which ice cream is least favored? _____

3. How many children voted? _____ children

4. Use the picture graph.
   How many children like blue best?

   Ⓐ 2 children

   Ⓑ 3 children

   Ⓒ 4 children

   Ⓓ 5 children

Favorite Colors		
☺☺☺☺	☺☺☺☺☺	☺☺
Red	Blue	Green

5. **Journal** What does the picture graph show?

_____

_____

_____

Building 1,000

Remember.

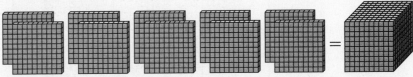

10 ones = _____ ten

10 tens = _____ hundred

10 hundreds = _____ thousand

Count by 100s to count hundreds.

Color the models to show the hundreds.

1. 2 hundreds
200

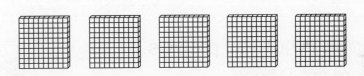

2. 3 hundreds
300

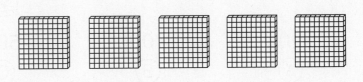

3. 4 hundreds
400

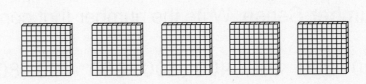

4. 5 hundreds
500

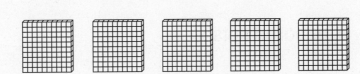

Building 1,000

Write how many. Use models if needed.

1.

100 less is

_____ .

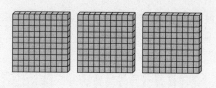

_____

100 more is

_____ .

2.

100 less is

_____ .

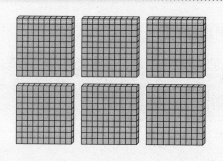

_____

100 more is

_____ .

3. Each bag has 100 pretzels.
There are 9 bags.
How many pretzels are there in all?

90	100	500	900
Ⓐ	Ⓑ	Ⓒ	Ⓓ

4. Number Sense Write the number that comes next:

100 200 300 400 500 600 700 800 900 _____
How many hundred flats would you need to show it?

_____ hundred flats

Counting Hundreds, Tens, and Ones

Use models and your workmat to sort and count.

First, put the hundreds models on your mat.
Next, put the tens models on your mat.
Then, put the ones models on your mat.

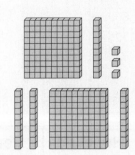

Write the number of hundreds, tens, and ones.

Hundreds	Tens	Ones
2	4	3

Write the numbers.
Use models and your workmat if needed.

1.

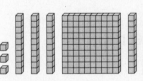

Hundreds	Tens	Ones

2.

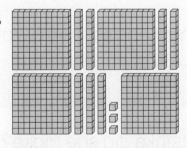

Hundreds	Tens	Ones

3. Number Sense How many hundreds are in 581? _____

Counting Hundreds, Tens, and Ones

Write the numbers. Use models and your workmat if needed.

1.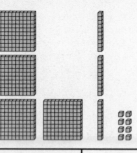

Hundreds	Tens	Ones
4	3	8

2.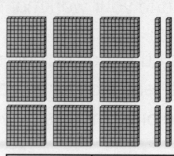

Hundreds	Tens	Ones

3.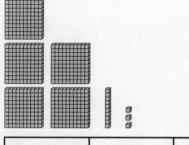

Hundreds	Tens	Ones

4.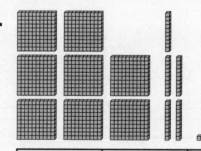

Hundreds	Tens	Ones

5. Reasonableness Kyra wrote **78** to match the model.

What mistake did she make?

_____

What is the correct number to match the model?

87   708   780   807
Ⓐ   Ⓑ   Ⓒ   Ⓓ

Reading and Writing Numbers to 1,000

Expanded form uses plus signs to show hundreds, tens, and ones.

200 + 60 + 4

You can draw models to show expanded form.

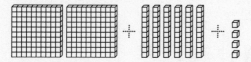

The **number word** is two hundred sixty-four.

The **standard form** is

264.

Draw models to show the expanded form.
Write the number in standard form.

1. 400 + 30 + 8   four hundred thirty-eight

   _____

2. 300 + 70 + 2   three hundred seventy-two

   _____

3. Write the number in expanded   five hundred fourteen
   and standard form.

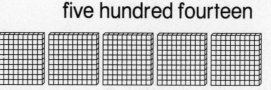

   _____ + _____ + _____   _____

Reading and Writing Numbers to 1,000

Circle the models to match the expanded form.
Then write the standard form.

1. 200 + 70 + 5

   two hundred
   seventy five

   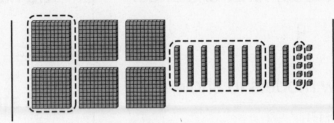

   275

2. 100 + 40 + 0

   one hundred
   forty

   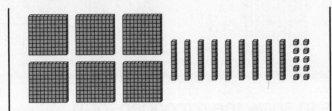

   _____

3. 300 + 60 + 2

   three hundred
   sixty two

   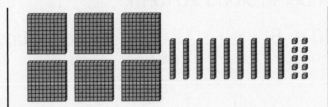

   _____

4. 329 cars are parked in a parking lot.

   What is the expanded form of 329?

   Ⓐ 200 + 90 + 3

   Ⓑ 200 + 20 + 9

   Ⓒ 300 + 20 + 9

   Ⓓ 300 + 90 + 2

5. **Reasoning** What is the greatest number you can make using these digits?

   5   7   2

   Ⓐ 257

   Ⓑ 572

   Ⓒ 725

   Ⓓ 752

Practice 17-3

Changing Numbers by Hundreds and Tens

When you change a number by adding or subtracting tens, the tens digit changes.

$100 + 30 + 6 = 136$

Use mental math to think: 10 more.

$136 + 10 =$ **146**

Use mental math to think: 20 less.

$136 - 20 =$ **116**

When you change a number by adding or subtracting hundreds, the hundreds digit changes.

$300 + 50 + 3 = 353$

Use mental math to think: 100 more.

$353 + 100 =$ **453**

Use mental math to think: 200 less.

$353 - 200 =$ **153**

1. Use models and mental math to solve.

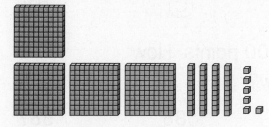

$400 + 40 + 6 = 446$

$446 + 20 \ =$ _____

$446 + 200 =$ _____

2. **Journal** Draw hundreds, tens, and ones models for 254. Show 10 more. Solve.

$254 + 10 =$ _____

Changing Numbers by Hundreds and Tens

Use models, drawings, or mental math to solve.
Write the numbers.

1. Start with 148.

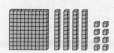

$148 + 40 = 188$

$148 + 400 = 548$

2. Start with 594.

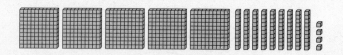

$594 - 30 = $ _____

$594 - 300 = $ _____

3. Suki has 350 points. She gets 30 more points.

How many points does Suki have now?

320	353	360	380
Ⓐ	Ⓑ	Ⓒ	Ⓓ

4. Abdul has 687 points. He loses 100 points. How many points does Abdul have now?

787	687	686	587
Ⓐ	Ⓑ	Ⓒ	Ⓓ

5. Algebra Write the number.

How many more hundreds do you need to make 500?

_____ + _____ = 500

Patterns with Numbers on Hundreds Charts

Pick a row on the top chart. Read the numbers across the row.

11	12	13	14	15	16	17	18	19	20
21	22	23	24	25	26	27	28	29	30
31	32	33	34	35	36	37	38	39	40

The ones go up by ____.

Pick a column and read the numbers from top to bottom.

110	111	112	113	114	115	116	117	118	119	120
210	211	212	213	214	215	216	217	218	219	220
310	311	312	313	314	315	316	317	318	319	320
410	411	412	413	414	415	416	417	418	419	420

The tens go up by ____.

In the bottom chart, the hundreds digits from top to bottom go up by ____.

Look at the digits. Look for a pattern.
Write the missing numbers.

1.

	33	34
42	43	
52	53	54

	77	78
86	87	
96		98

2.

43		45
53		55
		65

430		450
530		550
		650

3. **Number Sense** What is the rule?

60 ⟶ 70   670 ⟶ 680

Patterns with Numbers on Hundreds Charts

Write the missing numbers.

1.

52	53	54
62	63	64
72	73	74

520	530	
620		
		740

2.

		69
77	78	
		89

	680	
770		790
	880	

3.

15		
	26	
		37

	160	
250		
350		370

4. Which best describes the pattern of the numbers
on the mailboxes?

10 more	10 less	2 more	2 less
Ⓐ	Ⓑ	Ⓒ	Ⓓ

5. Number Sense Look for a pattern. What is the rule?

740   730   720   710

100 more	100 less	10 more	10 less
Ⓐ	Ⓑ	Ⓒ	Ⓓ

Comparing Numbers

Compare the digits with the greatest place value first.

125   243

100 is _less than_ 200. So, 125 243.

If the hundreds are equal, compare the tens.

243   217

40 is _more than_ 10. So, 243 217.

If the tens are equal, compare the ones.

217   216

7 is _more than_ 6. So, 217 216.

Compare.
Write <, >, or =.

1. 341 ◯ 432   **2.** 890 ◯ 880

3. 621 ◯ 639   **4.** 546 ◯ 546

Comparing Numbers

Compare. Write **greater than**, **less than**, or **equal to**.
Then write >, <, or =.

1. 157 is ___less than___ 214.   157 Ⓒ< 214

2. 600 is _____ 598.   600 ◯ 598

3. 771 is _____ 771.   771 ◯ 771

4. This week, 261 fans watched a soccer game.
   Last week, 216 fans watched a soccer game.
   Which comparison is correct?

   216 = 261   216 > 261   261 < 216   216 < 261
     Ⓐ   Ⓑ   Ⓒ   Ⓓ

5. **Spatial Thinking** Circle hundreds, tens, and ones
   to show your answer.

   This number is less than 200. The ones digit is
   5 less than 10. The tens digit is 2 more than the
   ones digit. What is the number?

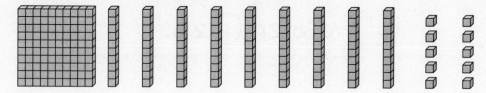

   _____

Before, After, and Between

Think about the order of numbers.

150	151	152	153	154	155	156	157	158	159
160	161	162	163	164	165	166	167	168	169

Use the words **before**, **after**, and **between** to
describe numbers.

_152_ is **before** 153   _168_ is **after** 167

_161_ is **between** 160 and 162

Use the number chart to help you write
the missing numbers.

300	301	302	303	304	305	306	307	308	309
310	311	312	313	314	315	316	317	318	319

Write the number that is one **before**.

I. _____, 304   _____, 314   _____, 319

Write the number that is one **after**.

2. 301, _____   307, _____   316, _____

Write the number that is **between**.

3. 300, _____, 302   314, _____, 316

4. **Journal** Write a riddle about a number. Use the
   words **before**, **after**, or **between** to give clues.

Before, After, and Between

Write the number that is one before.

1. 438 , 439   **2.** _____ , 624   **3.** _____ , 201

4. _____ , 516   **5.** _____ , 840   **6.** _____ , 111

Write the number that is one after.

7. 333, _____   **8.** 701, _____   **9.** 899, _____

10. 250, _____   **11.** 669, _____   **12.** 807, _____

Write the number that is between.

13. 518, _____ , 520   **14.** 299, _____ , 301

15. 393, _____ , 395   **16.** 747, _____ , 749

17. Monty picked a number card. The number is between 282 and 284.

What is the number?

281	283	285	823
Ⓐ	Ⓑ	Ⓒ	Ⓓ

18. Reasoning Which two numbers come after 297?

213, 298	751, 157	307, 299	200, 300
Ⓐ	Ⓑ	Ⓒ	Ⓓ

Ordering Numbers

Put the numbers in order from least to greatest.

| 273 | | 250 | | 499 |

Step 1. Compare the hundreds digits to find
the greatest number.
273   **2**50   **4**99

> 4 hundreds is greater than 2 hundreds.
> 499 is the greatest number.

Step 2. Then compare the tens digits.
2**7**3   2**5**0

> 7 tens is greater than 5 tens.
> So, 250 is the least number.

250 , *273* , *499*
 least   greatest

Write the numbers in order from least to greatest.

1. | 187 | 126 | 219 |

_____ , _____ , _____
   least   greatest

2. | 489 | 352 | 327 |

_____ , _____ , _____
   least   greatest

3. | 734 | 632 | 638 |

_____ , _____ , _____
   least   greatest

4. **Number Sense** Write three numbers in order
   from least to greatest.

_____ , _____ , _____
   least   greatest

Reteaching **17-8**

Ordering Numbers

Write the numbers in order from least to greatest.

1. 276 267 207

    2̲0̲7̲ , 2̲6̲7̲ , 2̲7̲6̲
    least   greatest

2. 16 600 60

    _____ , _____ , _____
    least   greatest

Write the numbers in order from greatest to least.

3. 986 789 892

    _____ , _____ , _____
    greatest   least

4. 377 737 773

    _____ , _____ , _____
    greatest   least

5. Which number is the least?

    529   531   560   528
    (A)   (B)   (C)   (D)

6. Which number is the greatest?

    120   102   110   100
    (A)   (B)   (C)   (D)

7. **Journal** Tell how you would decide which number
   is the greatest. Then circle it.

    572, 570, 576

    _____

    _____

Problem Solving: Look for a Pattern

Put these numbers in order from least to greatest.

How do the numbers change each time? Look for a pattern.

240   210   230   250   220

<u>210</u>, <u>220</u>, <u>230</u>, <u>240</u>, <u>250</u>

The pattern rule is <u>+10</u>.

Look for a number pattern to solve.

I.

305   310   300   315

Put the room number signs in order from least to greatest.

<u>300</u>, <u>305</u>,

_____, _____

The pattern rule is _____.

What room number would

come next? _____

2.

405   105   305   205

Put the taxis in order by number from least to greatest.

_____, _____,

_____, _____

The pattern rule is _____.

What taxi number would

come next? _____

Name _____

Problem Solving: Look for a Pattern

Look for a number pattern to solve.

1.

Put the numbers on the bears in order from least to greatest.

<u>616</u>, <u>636</u>,
<u>656</u>, _____

What is the pattern rule?

<u>+20</u>

What is the next number?

<u>696</u>

2.

Put the numbers on the geese in order from least to greatest.

_____, _____,

_____, _____

What is the pattern rule?

_____

What is the next number?

_____

---

3. What is the next mailbox number?

751	791	841	881
Ⓐ	Ⓑ	Ⓒ	Ⓓ

---

4. Algebra Look at the pattern. What is the missing number?

400, 425, _____, 475

470	465	450	435
Ⓐ	Ⓑ	Ⓒ	Ⓓ

Mentel Math

Use mental math to add these three-digit numbers: 315 + 200.
You just need to add the hundreds.
Only the hundreds digit will change.

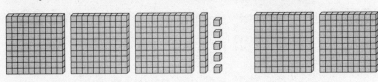

$$3|5 \qquad + \qquad 2 00 \qquad = \underline{5}|5$$

Add using mental math. Complete the addition sentence.

I. 323 + 200

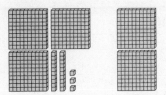

$$\underline{323} + 200 = \underline{523}$$

2. 281 + 400

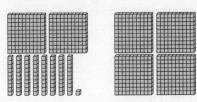

$$\underline{\hspace{2cm}} + 400 = \underline{\hspace{2cm}}$$

3. 193 + 500

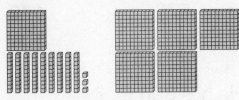

$$\underline{\hspace{2cm}} + 500 = \underline{\hspace{2cm}}$$

4. 487 + 300

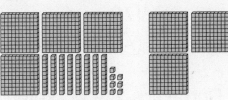

$$\underline{\hspace{2cm}} + 300 = \underline{\hspace{2cm}}$$

5. Add using mental math. Use models if needed.

$$560 + 300 = \underline{\hspace{2cm}}$$

Name _____

Mental Math

Add using mental math. Use models if you need to.

1.  and **300**

2. 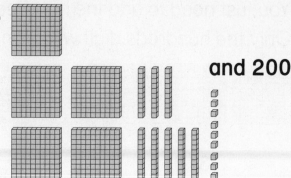 and **200**

$$\underline{413} + \underline{300} = \underline{713}$$

$$\underline{\hspace{1cm}} + \underline{\hspace{1cm}} = \underline{\hspace{1cm}}$$

3. $718 + 200 =$ _____

4. $605 + 300 =$ _____

5. $400 + 234 =$ _____

6. $600 + 241 =$ _____

7. Tanner has 500 star stickers. She has 179 rainbow stickers.
How many stickers does Tanner have in all?

479	500	579	679
Ⓐ	Ⓑ	Ⓒ	Ⓓ

8. Darrin has 274 basketball stickers. He has 300 football
stickers. How many stickers does Darrin have in all?

163	279	574	682
Ⓐ	Ⓑ	Ⓒ	Ⓓ

9. Algebra Write the missing numbers that make these
number sentences true.

$$400 + 500 = 600 + \underline{\hspace{1.5cm}}$$

$$\underline{\hspace{1.5cm}} = 899 + 100$$

Estimating Sums

You can estimate the sum of 135 + 337.
Is it greater than or less than 500?

One way to estimate:

Step 1: Add 300 to 135.

135 + 300 = __435__.

Step 2: Look at the tens and ones in 3**37**.

So, 435 + **37** is less than 500.

Another way to estimate:

Step 1: Add the hundreds in both numbers.

135 + 337 = __400__.

Step 2: Look at the tens in both numbers.

30 + 30 = 60
So, 400 + 60 is less than 500.

Follow the steps to estimate.

Is 179 + 267 greater than or less than 600?

1. Add 200 to 179. __179__ + __200__ = _____

2. Look at the tens and ones in 2**67**. Then circle greater than or less than.

379 + 67 is   greater than
                          600.
                less than

Choose a way to estimate. Circle greater than or less than.

3.   is   greater than
237 + 417   600.
                      less than

Name _____

Estimating Sums

Do the two buckets have more cherries or fewer
cherries than the tub can hold? Circle more or fewer.

1.    (more)   fewer

2.    more   fewer

3.    more   fewer

4. There are 314 apples in baskets. There are 281 apples
still on the trees. Are there 600 apples in all? Explain.

_____

5. One week, a group of chimpanzees ate 437 bananas.
The next week, they ate 465 bananas. Did they eat more
than 900 bananas during both weeks? Explain.

_____

6. **Estimation** Which problem has a sum that is less than 400?

329 + 161   216 + 251   245 + 198   262 + 126

Models for Adding with Three-Digit Numbers

$135 + 248 =$ _____

Step 1: Add the ones. Regroup if you need to.

Step 2: Add the tens. Regroup if you need to.

Step 3: Add the hundreds.

	Hundreds	Tens	Ones
135			
248			

$5 + 8 = 13$ ones.
Regroup 10 ones
for 1 ten.

$135 + 248 =$ <u>383</u>

Add to find the sum.

Use models and your workmat.

1.

Hundreds	Tens	Ones

$341 + 127 =$ _____

2.

Hundreds	Tens	Ones

$524 + 249 =$ _____

Models for Adding with Three-Digit Numbers

Add. Regroup if needed.

1.

Hundreds	Tens	Ones
□	1	
6	3	4
+ 2	1	8
8	5	2

2.

Hundreds	Tens	Ones
□	□	
5	9	3
+ 1	3	9

3.

Hundreds	Tens	Ones
□	□	
7	6	5
+ 1	8	0

4.

Hundreds	Tens	Ones
□	□	
3	5	6
+ 4	3	4

5.

Hundreds	Tens	Ones
□	□	
2	7	6
+ 5	9	3

6.

Hundreds	Tens	Ones
□	□	
4	4	1
+ 1	9	9

7. A fire truck traveled 267 miles in July to put out fires.

It traveled 398 miles in August to put out fires.

Which problem shows the total number of miles for both months?

Ⓐ
```
  1 1
  2 6 7
+ 3 9 8
  6 6 5
```

Ⓑ
```
  1 1
  2 7 6
+ 3 9 8
  6 7 4
```

Ⓒ
```
  1
  2 6 7
+ 3 9 8
  6 5 5
```

Ⓓ
```
  1
  2 6 7
+ 3 9 8
  5 6 5
```

8. Reasonableness George thinks that 515 plus 381 is 896.

Markita says that George forgot to regroup.

Do you have to regroup to add 515 and 381? Explain.

_____

Adding Three-Digit Numbers

Step 1: Add the ones. Regroup if you need to.

Step 2: Add the tens. Regroup if you need to.

Step 3: Add the hundreds.

Think:
Regroup 10 tens
for 1 hundred.

$163 + 174 =$ ___?___

Hundreds	Tens	Ones

Hundreds	Tens	Ones
	1	6	3

Hundreds	Tens	Ones
1	6	3
+ 1	7	4
3	3	7

Draw to regroup. Add.

1. $218 + 136 =$ ___?___

Hundreds	Tens	Ones

Hundreds	Tens	Ones
2	1	8
+ 1	3	6

Add. Use models and your workmat.

2.

Hundreds	Tens	Ones
1	2	5
+ 2	4	2

3.

Hundreds	Tens	Ones
4	1	9
+ 2	5	6

Adding Three-Digit Numbers

Add. Use models if needed.

1.   472
   + 347

2.   609
   + 166

3.   267
   + 228

4.   473
   + 338

5.   314
   + 599

6.   186
   + 357

7.   487
   + 512

8.   225
   + 135

9.   235
   + 146

10.   465
   + 264

11.   308
   + 238

12.   356
   + 29

13. One summer, an airplane made 326 trips.
The next summer, the airplane made 392 trips.
How many trips did the airplane make during both summers?

192   618   718   798
Ⓐ   Ⓑ   Ⓒ   Ⓓ

14. **Reasoning** Caitlin's paper shows
how she added 345 and 271.
What mistake did she make?

   345
   + 271
   516

_____

_____

Mental Math: Ways to Find Missing Parts

Count on by hundreds and tens to find the parts of the whole.

260 + _____ = 700

First, count on by hundreds.   _4_ hundreds

260, _360_, _460_ _560_, _660_

   100   200   300   400

Next, count on by tens.   _4_ tens

660, _670_, _680_ _690_, _700_

   10   20   30   40

4 hundreds and 4 tens is 440.

So, 260 + _440_ = 700

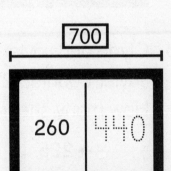

700

| 260 | 440 |

I. 350 + _?_ = 600

Count on by hundreds.   _____ hundreds

350, _____, _____

Count on by tens.   _____ tens

550, _____, _____, _____, _____, _____

_____ hundreds and _____ tens is _____.

So, 350 + _____ = 600

Mental Math: Ways to Find Missing Parts

Count on or count back to find the missing part.
Write the number.

1. $420 + \underline{540} = 960$

| 960 |

| 420 | 540 |

2. $\underline{\hspace{2cm}} + 190 = 630$

| 630 |

| 190 | |

3. Clyde and Javier counted a total of 450 sheep.
Javier counted 225 sheep.
How many sheep did Clyde count?

| 225 | 250 | 325 | 450 |
| (A) | (B) | (C) | (D) |

4. Geometry Which weight is needed to balance the scale?

 150
(A)

  200
(B)

  250
(C)

  125
(D)

Estimating Differences

Estimate the difference: 596 − 221.

First, find the nearest hundred.
Is 596 closer to 500 or 600?   600

Is 221 closer to 200 or 300?   200

Then, subtract.

600 − 200 = 400

So, 596 − 221 is about 400.

Estimate each difference. First, find the nearest hundred.
Then circle the estimate that matches the problem.

1. 502 − 105   is about   200   300   (400)

   500 − 100 = ?

2. 609 − 403   is about   200   300   400

   _____ − _____ = ?

3. 511 − 298   is about   100   200   300

   _____ − _____ = ?

4. **Number Sense** 881 − 500   is about _____.

Estimating Differences

Circle the problem that matches the estimate.

1. about 200   820 − 205   or   (421 − 196)

2. about 400   637 − 231   or   794 − 512

3. about 300   679 − 199   or   916 − 593

4. about 600   909 − 287   or   726 − 204

5. Marcus has to put about 100 cans on a shelf
   to finish his job. Which box of cans should
   he put on the shelf?

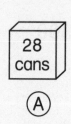
28 cans
Ⓐ

112 cans
Ⓑ

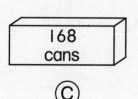
168 cans
Ⓒ

193 cans
Ⓓ

6. **Estimation** Cowhand Dusty put 203 cows
   inside of the fences. There are 694 cows
   in the herd. About how many more cows
   does Dusty need to put inside of the fences?

   Ⓐ about 300 cows

   Ⓑ about 400 cows

   Ⓒ about 500 cows

   Ⓓ about 600 cows

Practice 18-6

Models for Subtracting with Three-Digit Numbers

327 − 164 = ___?___

Step 1: Subtract the ones. Regroup if you need to.

Step 2: Subtract the tens. Regroup if you need to.

Step 3: Subtract the hundreds.

Regroup
1 hundred
for 10 tens

Hundreds	Tens	Ones

327 − 164 = __163__

Subtract to find the difference.

Use models and your workmat.

1.

Hundreds	Tens	Ones

549 − 295 = _____

2.

Hundreds	Tens	Ones

835 − 516 = _____

Name _____

Models for Subtracting with Three-Digit Numbers

Use models and your workmat. Subtract. Regroup if needed.

1.

Hundreds	Tens	Ones
6	15	
7	5	5
− 2	8	2
4	7	3

2.

Hundreds	Tens	Ones
4	8	5
− 1	3	9

3.

Hundreds	Tens	Ones
5	7	8
− 2	9	7

4.

Hundreds	Tens	Ones
6	5	7
− 1	2	8

5.

Hundreds	Tens	Ones
7	3	2
− 4	5	8

6.

Hundreds	Tens	Ones
9	2	7
− 3	0	4

7. One building is 332 feet tall. Another building is 208 feet tall. How much higher is the first building?

540 feet Ⓐ 136 feet Ⓑ 134 feet Ⓒ 124 feet Ⓓ

8. Spatial Thinking Use the model to help you subtract.

A farm has 319 animals.
136 of the animals are pigs.
How many animals are not pigs?

_____ animals are not pigs.

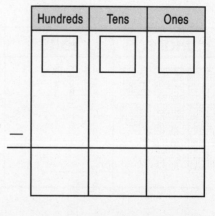

Hundreds	Tens	Ones
−		

Subtracting Three-Digit Numbers

Step 1: Subtract the ones. Regroup if you need to.
Step 2: Subtract the tens. Regroup if you need to.
Step 3: Subtract the hundreds.

Think: Regroup 1 ten for 10 ones.

362 − 125 = __?__

Hundreds	Tens	Ones

Hundreds	Tens	Ones
	5	12
3	6	2
− 1	2	5
2	3	7

Draw to regroup. Subtract.

1. 429 − 174 = __?__

Hundreds	Tens	Ones

Hundreds	Tens	Ones
4	2	9
− 1	7	4

Subtract. Use models and your workmat if needed.

2.

Hundreds	Tens	Ones
5	7	4
− 2	1	3

3.

Hundreds	Tens	Ones
7	8	8
− 2	6	9

Subtracting Three-Digit Numbers

Subtract. Use models if needed.

1. 426
   − 271

2. 659
   − 372

3. 953
   − 209

4. 390
   − 126

5. 562
   − 129

6. 486
   − 357

7. 917
   − 582

8. 625
   − 135

9. 589
   − 193

10. 707
    − 264

11. 643
    − 228

12. 356
    − 29

13. There were 926 wild horses in a valley. Then 456 horses ran away. How many horses are left in the valley?

530 (A) 582 (B) 470 (C) 469 (D)

14. **Number Sense** Use these numbers only once to finish the two subtraction problems. Then subtract.

2 5 7 1 4 6

Make the greatest difference.   Make the least difference.

9 5 0   9 5 0

Problem Solving: Make a Graph

Grade 2 collected 100
pop tops on Tuesday and
300 on Wednesday.
Add this data to the table.

Pop Tops Collected			
	Monday	Tuesday	Wednesday
Grade 1	150	100	200
Grade 2	200	100	300

Show the data on a bar graph.

First, add the pop tops collected on Monday.

150 + 200 = 350

Then, color the Monday column to show 350 cans were collected.

Next, do the same for Tuesday and Wednesday.

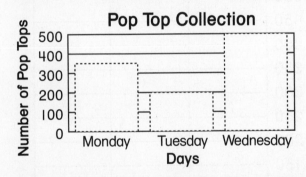

Use the graph to answer the questions.

1. How many pop tops were collected on Tuesday? _____

2. How many pop tops were collected on Wednesday? _____

3. **Number Sense** If Grade 2 collected 200 pop
tops on Tuesday, how would the graph change?

_____

Problem Solving: Make a Graph

Use the chart to answer the questions.

1. How many crayons are there in all?

   <u>750</u> crayons

Art Supplies			
	Crayons	Paints	Brushes
Art Room 1	350	200	300
Art Room 2	400	150	250

2. How many paints are there in all?

   _____ paints

3. How many brushes are there in all?

   _____ brushes

4. Use your answers from Exercises 1-3 to complete the graph. Show how many crayons, paints, and brushes there are in both rooms.

5. Together, which art supply do the two art rooms have the most of?

   clay Ⓐ   crayons Ⓑ   paints Ⓒ   brushes Ⓓ

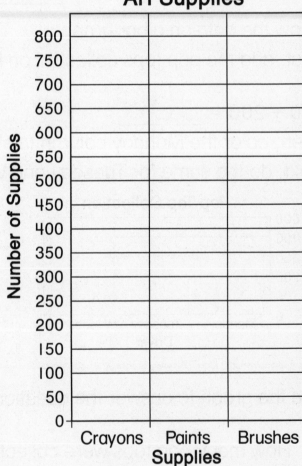

Art Supplies

6. **Journal** How is a bar graph different from a chart?

_____

Repeated Addition and Multiplication

Add equal groups to find how many in all.
Multiply equal groups to find how many in all.

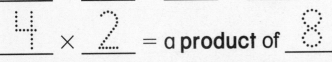

_2_ + _2_ + _2_ + _2_ = a **sum** of _8_

_4_ × _2_ = a **product** of _8_

> 4 × 2 means
> 4 times 2

I. Number Sense Draw dots to show equal groups.
Find the sum and the product.

$3 + 3 + 3 =$ _____

$3 \times 3 =$ _____

□ □ □

Find the sum and the product.

2.

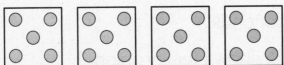

$5 + 5 + 5 + 5 + 5 =$ _____ $5 \times 5 =$ _____

3.

$4 + 4 + 4 + 4 =$ _____ $4 \times 4 =$ _____

Repeated Addition and Multiplication

Use the model.
Complete each sentence.

1. ? in all

$1 + 1 + 1 + 1 + 1 = \underline{5}$

$5 \times 1 = \underline{5}$

2. ? in all

$6 + 6 = \underline{\hspace{1cm}}$

$2 \times 6 = \underline{\hspace{1cm}}$

3. ? in all

$3 + 3 + 3 = \underline{\hspace{1cm}}$

$3 \times 3 = \underline{\hspace{1cm}}$

4. ? in all

$6 + 6 + 6 = \underline{\hspace{1cm}}$

$3 \times 6 = \underline{\hspace{1cm}}$

5. 2 monkeys climb a tree.
Each monkey picks 3 bananas.

Which number sentence shows this problem?

$2 + 3$	2×2	2×3	3×3
Ⓐ	Ⓑ	Ⓒ	Ⓓ

6. Number Sense Find the sum.
Write a multiplication sentence to
show the same amount.

$5 + 5 + 5 + 5 = \underline{\hspace{1cm}}$

$\underline{\hspace{1cm}} \times \underline{\hspace{1cm}} = \underline{\hspace{1cm}}$

Building Arrays

A collection of objects arranged in equal rows and columns
is an **array.** You can use an **array** to show equal groups.

Array

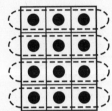

Circle each row. Count the number of rows.

There are ___4___ rows.

Count the number of dots in each row.

There are ___3___ dots in each row.

Write the multiplication sentence.

___4___ × ___3___ = ___12___
rows   in each row   product

Circle each row. Count the number of rows.
Count the number of dots in each row.
Write the multiplication sentence.

1.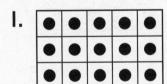

There are _____ rows.

There are _____ dots in each row.

_____ × _____ = _____
rows   in each row   product

2.

There are _____ rows.

There are _____ dots in each row.

_____ × _____ = _____
rows   in each row   product

Building Arrays

Write the multiplication sentence.

1.

$$\underline{}3 \times \underline{}2 = \underline{}6$$
rows   columns   product

2.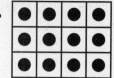

$$\underline{} \times \underline{} = \underline{}$$
rows   columns   product

3.

$$\underline{} \times \underline{} = \underline{}$$
rows   columns   product

4.

$$\underline{} \times \underline{} = \underline{}$$
rows   columns   product

5. Mrs. Rose takes cookies out of the oven.
   They are in 4 rows and 5 columns.

   Which multiplication sentence
   shows how many cookies in all?

   4×4 4×5 4×6 5×5
   Ⓐ   Ⓑ   Ⓒ   Ⓓ

6. **Spatial Thinking** Draw an array with 2 rows and
   4 columns. Then write a number sentence for your array.

   $$\underline{} \times \underline{} = \underline{}$$
   rows   columns   product

Writing Multiplication Stories

You can draw a picture and write a story to show 2×3.

Draw 2 fish tanks.

Draw 3 fish in each tank.

Solve the story.

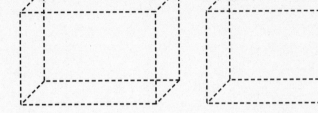

There are ___2___ tanks.

There are ___3___ fish in each tank.

How many fish in all? $2 \times 3 = $ ___6___

Finish the picture and the story for 6×3.

1.

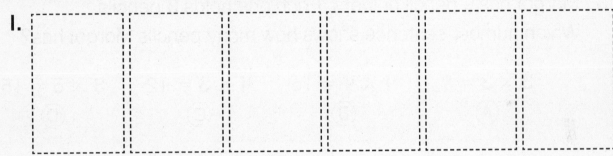

There are ___6___ boxes.

There are _____ in each box.

How many _____ in all? $6 \times 3 = $ _____

....

2. Journal Draw a picture and write a story about 4×2.

Reteaching 19-3

Writing Multiplication Stories

Draw a picture. Write a story and solve.

1. $4 \times 2 =$ __8__

_____

_____

_____

2. $5 \times 3 =$ _____

_____

_____

_____

3. Margot has 4 pencil holders. Each one holds 3 pencils.
Which number sentence shows how many pencils Margot has?

$3 \times 3 = 9$ $4 \times 4 = 16$ $4 \times 3 = 12$ $3 \times 5 = 15$
  Ⓐ   Ⓑ   Ⓒ   Ⓓ

4. Journal Jeb drew this picture to show 3×8.
Write a story about the picture. Solve.

_____

_____

_____

$3 \times 8 =$ _____

Vertical Form

You can write multiplication sentences in two ways.

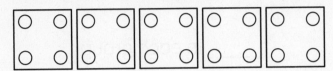

> Across is called **horizontal** form.
> Down is called **vertical** form.

Across × = 20
groups   in each   product
           group

Down
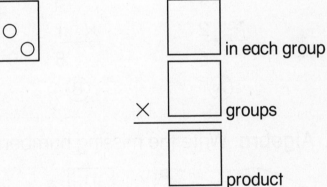
4 — in each group
× 5 — groups
_____
20 — product

Fill in the factors. Then write the product.

1.
[four boxes each with 3 circles]

_____ × _____ = _____
groups   in each   product
         group

[vertical boxes]
☐ in each group
× ☐ groups
_____
☐ product

2.
[five boxes each with 2 dots]

_____ × _____ = _____
groups   in each   product
         group

[vertical boxes]
☐ in each group
× ☐ groups
_____
☐ product

Reteaching **19-4**

Vertical Form

Fill in the factors.
Then write the product.

1. 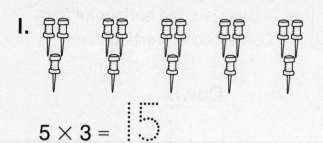 _____ in each group

      × _____ groups

   $5 \times 3 =$ **15**   _____ in all

2. There are 2 boxes. 4 markers are in each box.
Which problem shows how many markers in all?

$$\begin{array}{r} 4 \\ +\ 2 \\ \hline 6 \end{array}$$
Ⓐ

$$\begin{array}{r} 8 \\ \times\ 1 \\ \hline 8 \end{array}$$
Ⓑ

$$\begin{array}{r} 4 \\ \times\ 2 \\ \hline 8 \end{array}$$
Ⓒ

$$\begin{array}{r} 2 \\ +\ 2 \\ \hline 4 \end{array}$$
Ⓓ

3. **Algebra** Write the missing numbers.

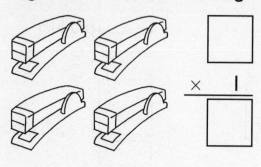

$$\begin{array}{r} \square \\ \times\quad 1 \\ \hline \square \end{array}$$

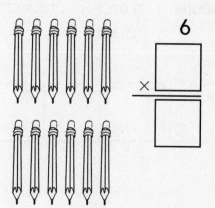

$$\begin{array}{r} 6 \\ \times\quad\ \\ \hline \square \end{array}$$

Multiplying in Any Order

You can multiply numbers in any order and get the same product.

Use counters to make 3 rows with 2 counters in each row.

Rearrange your counters. Make 2 rows with 3 counters in each row.

2 and 3 are factors.
3 × 2 is the same as 2 × 3.

3 × $\underset{\substack{\text{in each} \\ \text{row}}}{\underline{2}}$ = $\underset{\text{product}}{\underline{6}}$
$\underset{\text{rows}}{}$

2 × $\underset{\substack{\text{in each} \\ \text{row}}}{\underline{3}}$ = $\underset{\text{product}}{\underline{6}}$
$\underset{\text{rows}}{}$

Use counters to make the arrays.
Write the multiplication sentence for each array.

1.

$\underset{\text{rows}}{\underline{\hspace{1cm}}}$ × $\underset{\substack{\text{in each} \\ \text{row}}}{\underline{\hspace{1cm}}}$ = $\underset{\text{product}}{\underline{\hspace{1cm}}}$

$\underset{\text{rows}}{\underline{\hspace{1cm}}}$ × $\underset{\substack{\text{in each} \\ \text{row}}}{\underline{\hspace{1cm}}}$ = $\underset{\text{product}}{\underline{\hspace{1cm}}}$

2.

$\underset{\text{rows}}{\underline{\hspace{1cm}}}$ × $\underset{\substack{\text{in each} \\ \text{row}}}{\underline{\hspace{1cm}}}$ = $\underset{\text{product}}{\underline{\hspace{1cm}}}$

$\underset{\text{rows}}{\underline{\hspace{1cm}}}$ × $\underset{\substack{\text{in each} \\ \text{row}}}{\underline{\hspace{1cm}}}$ = $\underset{\text{product}}{\underline{\hspace{1cm}}}$

3. Journal Draw a picture to show that the product of 5 × 2 and 2 × 5 is the same.

Multiplying in Any Order

Complete the sentence for each grid.

1.

$\underline{3} \times \underline{4} = \underline{12}$

rows   in each   product
row

_____ × _____ = _____

rows   in each   product
row

2.

_____ × _____ = _____

rows   in each   product
row

_____ × _____ = _____

rows   in each   product
row

Which number sentence fits the grid?

3.

$2 \times 5 = 10$ $2 \times 6 = 12$ $2 \times 7 = 14$ $3 \times 6 = 18$
Ⓐ   Ⓑ   Ⓒ   Ⓓ

4. **Reasonableness** Write multiplication sentences.

_____ × _____ = _____   _____ × _____ = _____

Do both grids show the same number? _____

Problem Solving: Draw a Picture and Write a Number Sentence

You can draw a picture to solve a problem.

First, read the problem.

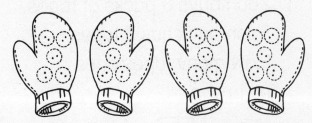

Fran knits 4 mittens.

Each mitten has 5 buttons.

How many buttons are there in all?

Next, draw 5 buttons on each mitten.

Then, write a number sentence.

$$\underline{4} \times \underline{5} = \underline{20}$$

mittens × buttons on each mitten = buttons in all

Draw a picture to solve.

Then write a number sentence.

1. There are 6 vases.

    Each vase has 3 flowers.

    How many flowers are there in all?

_____ × _____ = _____ flowers in all.

Problem Solving: Draw a Picture and Write a Number Sentence

Write number sentences to solve the problem.
Make part-part-whole drawings to help.

1. Zach buys 3 packs of tapes.
   Each pack has 3 tapes.
   How many tapes does
   he buy in all?

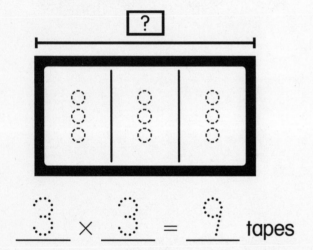

$\underline{3} \times \underline{3} = \underline{9}$ tapes

2. Carlos makes 2 books.
   Each book has 6 pages.
   How many pages did
   Carlos make in all?

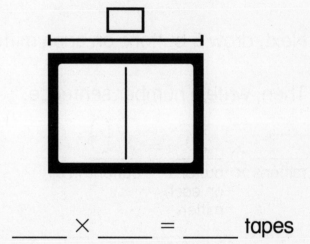

____ × ____ = ____ tapes

3. Nell has 2 baskets. She has 9 toys in each basket.
   How many toys does she have in all?

16 toys	17 toys	18 toys	19 toys
Ⓐ	Ⓑ	Ⓒ	Ⓓ

4. **Reasoning** Which number sentence will solve the problem?

   The flute section of a marching band has 4 rows.
   It has 5 players in each row. How many people
   are in the flute section?

$4 \times 4 = 16$	$4 \times 5 = 20$	$4 \times 6 = 24$	$5 \times 5 = 25$
Ⓐ	Ⓑ	Ⓒ	Ⓓ

Division as Sharing

5 children want to share 10 counters equally. Draw 1 counter for each child. Keep drawing 1 counter for each child until you have drawn 10 counters in all.

If each child gets the same number of counters, each gets an **equal share.**

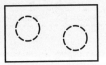
Brandon

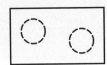
Melissa

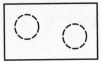
Joaquin

Dorothea

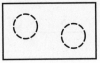
Janet

There are __10__ counters to share equally.

There are __5__ groups of counters.

There are __2__ counters in each group.

Each child gets __2__ counters.

Draw to show equal groups.
Write how many each child gets.

1. 4 children want to share 12 counters.

Gabriel

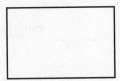
Talia

Shane

Natanya

Each child gets _____ counters.

Division as Sharing

Make equal groups. Write the numbers.

1. 15 crackers shared by 3 friends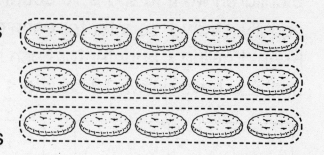

   __15__ in all

   __3__ groups of __5__ crackers

2. 12 books shared by 4 friends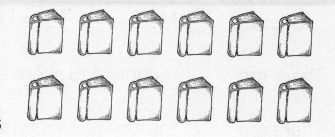

   _____ in all

   _____ groups of _____ books

3. 21 fish are shared equally by 7 bear cubs.
   How many fish does each bear cub get?

1	2	3	4
Ⓐ	Ⓑ	Ⓒ	Ⓓ

4. **Number Sense** You have 18 plums. Can you find
   6 different ways to show equal groups?

   _____ group of _____   _____ groups of _____

   _____ groups of _____   _____ groups of _____

   _____ groups of _____   _____ groups of _____

Division as Repeated Subtraction

Subtract over and over to solve.

Erin has 15 blueberries.
She puts 5 blueberries in
each pancake. How many
pancakes can she make?

$$15 - 5 = 10$$
$$10 - 5 = 5$$
$$5 - 5 = 0$$

How many times did you subtract to get to 0? __3__

How many pancakes can Erin make?

__3__ pancakes

Subtract over and over to solve.
Use counters to help you.

1. Gina has 12 carrots. If she
   puts 4 carrots in each
   plastic bag, how many
   bags will she fill?

   $$12 - 4 = \underline{}$$
   $$\underline{} - \underline{} = \underline{}$$
   $$\underline{} - \underline{} = \underline{}$$

   ____ bags

2. Kofi has 20 grapes.
   If he gives grapes to
   5 friends, how many
   grapes will each friend get?

   $$\underline{} - \underline{} = \underline{}$$
   $$\underline{} - \underline{} = \underline{}$$
   $$\underline{} - \underline{} = \underline{}$$
   $$\underline{} - \underline{} = \underline{}$$

   ____ grapes

Name _____

Division as Repeated Subtraction

Use counters. Subtract over and over. Write the numbers.

1. Moira has 12 postcards.
She writes 4 postcards each day.
How many days until the
postcards are gone?

$$12 - 4 = 8$$
$$8 - 4 = 4$$
$$4 - 4 = 0$$

__3__ days

2. Jesse has 20 quarters. He spends
5 quarters each day for lunch.
How many days until the quarters
are gone?

_____ − _____ = _____

_____ − _____ = _____

_____ − _____ = _____

_____ − _____ = _____

_____ days

Subtract over and over to solve. Use counters if you need to.

3. Imani has 16 straws. He gives 4 straws to each friend.
How many friends get straws?

2 Ⓐ   3 Ⓑ   4 Ⓒ   5 Ⓓ

4. Reasoning Anita has 14 apples.
She puts 2 apples on each plate.
How many plates does Anita need?

2 Ⓐ   4 Ⓑ   6 Ⓒ   7 Ⓓ

Writing Division Stories

Look at the picture.
Read the story.
Then write a division sentence.

There are 15 pilots.
There are an equal number
of pilots in 5 planes.
How many pilots are in each plane?

$$\underset{\text{pilots}}{15} \div \underset{\text{planes}}{5} = \underset{\text{pilots in each plane}}{3}$$

15 divided by 5 is 3.

Look at the picture. Complete the story.
Use the picture to solve the division sentence.

1. A plane has 24 seats in one section.

   There are ⋯3⋯ seats in each row.
   How many rows of seats are there?

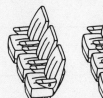

   24 ÷ 3 = _____ rows of seats

2. **Journal** Write a division story for the number sentence
   16 ÷ 4 = _____. Solve the division sentence.

Name _____

Writing Division Stories

Draw a picture for the problem.
Then write a division sentence.

1. Alma has 9 shirts. She has
   3 drawers. She puts the same
   number of shirts in each drawer.
   How many shirts does she put
   in each drawer?

   $\underline{9} \div \underline{3} = \underline{3}$

   $\underline{3}$ shirts

2. Felix divides 14 comic books into 2 piles.
   Which shows how many comic books are in each pile?

2	4	7	9
Ⓐ	Ⓑ	Ⓒ	Ⓓ

3. **Journal** Draw a picture. Write a story.
   Use the picture to solve the problem.

   _____

   _____

   _____

   _____

   _____

   $18 \div 3 =$ _____

Relating Multiplication and Division

Zoe put 12 apples in baskets.
She put 3 apples in each.
How many baskets did she use?

$12 \div 3 =$ ___?___

Multiplication can help you solve the problem.
Zoe has 12 apples in 4 groups of 3.

So, __3__ $\times$ __4__ = __12__

There are 3 apples in __4__ baskets. $12 \div 3 =$ __4__

Draw a picture to solve. Write the
multiplication sentence that helps you solve.
Then write the division sentence.

1. Karl puts 10 balls on shelves.
   There are 5 balls on each shelf.
   How many shelves does Karl fill?

   $5 \times$ __2__ = 10

   $10 \div 5 =$ ___?___   ___ $\div$ ___ = ___

2. Julio has 16 cards.
   He puts 4 cards in each row.
   How many rows are there?

   $4 \times$ ___ = ___

   $16 \div 4 =$ ___?___   ___ $\div$ ___ = ___

Reteaching 20-4

Relating Multiplication and Division

Complete each sentence. Use counters if you need to.

1. $2 \times \underline{8} = 16$

   $16 \div 2 = \underline{8}$

2. $4 \times \underline{} = 20$

   $20 \div 4 = \underline{}$

3. $4 \times \underline{} = 12$

   $12 \div 4 = \underline{}$

4. $7 \times \underline{} = 21$

   $21 \div 7 = \underline{}$

5. $5 \times \underline{} = 25$

   $25 \div 5 = \underline{}$

6. $9 \times \underline{} = 18$

   $18 \div 9 = \underline{}$

7. $4 \times \underline{} = 8$

   $8 \div 4 = \underline{}$

8. $5 \times \underline{} = 15$

   $15 \div 5 = \underline{}$

9. Which array shows both $2 \times 3 = 6$ and $6 \div 2 = 3$?

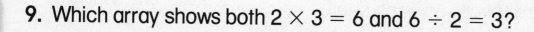

Ⓐ   Ⓑ   Ⓒ   Ⓓ

10. **Algebra** Which multiplication sentence will help you complete $24 \div 8 = \underline{}$?

 $4 \times 4 = 8$ $8 \times 3 = 24$ $8 \times 4 = 32$ $8 \times 8 = 64$

Ⓐ   Ⓑ   Ⓒ   Ⓓ

Problem Solving: Make a Table and Look for a Pattern

Matt is making sandwiches.
The number of slices of
bread he uses is the **input.**
The number of sandwiches
he makes is the **output.**

Input	2	4	6	8
Output	1	2	3	?

Matt uses 2 slices of bread for each sandwich.
How many sandwiches can Matt make from 8 slices of bread?

Look for a pattern in the table to help you.
The pattern, or rule, is to divide the **input** by 2.
So, if Matt uses 8 slices of bread,

$8 \div 2 = \underline{4}$.

Look for a pattern and complete the table.
Use the table to solve the problem.

Ira buys bunches of
bananas. There are
5 bananas in each bunch.

Input (bunches)	1	2	3	4	5
Output (bananas)	5	10	15		

1. What is the rule? ___multiply by 5___

2. How many bananas are there in 1 bunch? _____

3. How many bananas are there in 4 bunches? _____

Problem Solving: Make a Table and Look for a Pattern

1. Complete the table and look for a pattern.
   Then use the table to solve the problems.

Input	1	2	3	4	5
Output	5	10	15		

2. Ling cuts 3 stars out of paper. Each star has 5 points. How many points are there in all?

   _____ points

3. What is the rule?

   _____

4. How many points are there in 5 stars? _____

5. **Spatial Thinking** Complete the table.

Input	1	2			
Output	3	6			

What is the rule for the table?

(A) Add 3.

(B) Multiply by 6.

(C) Multiply by 3.

(D) Divide by 15.